PRECAST WALL PANELS

ACI SPECIAL PUBLICATIONS

SYMPOSIUM ON PRECAST CONCRETE WALL PANELS

A symposium of seven papers on various aspects of precast concrete wall panels, five of which were presented at the 60th Annual ACI Convention, Houston, Texas, March 4, 1964.

american concrete institute
P. O. BOX 4754, REDFORD STATION
DETROIT, MICHIGAN   48219

PUBLICATION SP-11

PREFACE

The precast architectural concrete panel field has grown rapidly in the last few years. While precast architectural concrete units or sections are really not new to the architectural, engineering, and construction industries, their use has never enjoyed such a wide acceptance as now.

The absence of recognized published data on specifications for precast concrete materials prompted the Technical Activities Committee of the American Concrete Institute to establish Committee 533, Precast Panels. The first organizational meeting was held at the 58th Annual Convention, Denver, March, 1962.

The Committee first pin-pointed problem areas of concern to architects, engineers, material suppliers, and the manufacturers of precast concrete panels. It appeared best to break the Committee into various subcommittees, each assigned to one of six general areas to be investigated first, with the provision that others might be added as committee action developed. These subcommittees concerned themselves with design, methods of fabrication, materials, types of precast concrete panels, tests on precast concrete panels, and miscellaneous items not covered wholly in the other five subcommittees.

Specifically, the subcommittee in charge of design is considering such items as structural and architectural design, various types of connections and fastenings, strength of concrete, and tolerances needed for design criteria. The subcommittee on methods of manufacturing is covering various ways to manufacture precast concrete along with the curing of the concrete, erection of the panels, together with problems with the various connections, fastenings, and tolerances as these effect the manufacturer of the panels. The subcommittee on materials is considering the quality of the concrete, and the items that go into making up the concrete. The subcommittee on types of precast panels is considering such items as plain panels, decorative panels, natural stone faced panels, load-bearing panels, non load-bearing panels, as sandwich panels, solid panels, ribbed panels, and any others that may come before them as they study this matter. The subcommittee on tests has studied control tests in the laboratory and in the field, as well as the manufacturing plant, and will investigate items on which additional research may be indicated. Finally, the subcommittee on miscellaneous items is picking up those items which have not been fully considered in the other subcommittees or which may properly effect work of all the subcommittees. Such items are studies of durability, the effect of air-entrainment and admixtures on the concrete, coatings on the finished panels, joint materials, coloring, and texture. Of course, each member of the entire Committee is active in several of the subcommittees and, therefore, there is ample opportunity to cross-check the work being done by each subcommittee.

The subcommittee on tests published a progress report, "Tests for Precast Concrete Wall Panels," in the ACI JOURNAL which is reprinted in the Appendix to this volume.

The papers presented in this Symposium are intended to be informative, but not necessarily the final conclusions of ACI Committee 533. These contributions will eventually lead to an official committee report.

William A. Cordon, Chairman
ACI Committee 533

ACI COMMITTEE 533
Precast Panels

William A. Cordon
Chairman
Richard C. Adams
Richard A. Backus
Paul Buehner
Joseph O. Florian
Steven Galezewski
A. C. Geelhoed
P. W. Gutmann
T. W. Hunt
D. P. Jenny

J. A. Hanson
Secretary
Victor F. Leabu
C. W. Meyer
Navin Pandya
W. H. F. Saia
Sheng Pao Sheng
I. J. Speyer
J. E. Stanners
H. T. Swanson
C. D. Wailes, Jr

CONTENTS

HISTORICAL REVIEW

Reviews the development of precast concrete wall panels. Discusses early exposed aggregate work, panel shape, use of color, structural panels, sandwich panels, and shocked concrete.

Precast Concrete Wall Panels:

Historical Review

By T. W. Hunt

■IT IS A COMMON MISTAKE to think of precast concrete panels as a recent development; say, of the past ten years. Actually, limited use of panels started prior to 1912 when units were cast at the job site and tilted into place. Similar methods were used for several housing developments and buildings of various occupancies built between 1912 and 1940. Growth in the use and variety of panels has been so spectacular in recent years, that it has overshadowed much of the earlier work.

EARLY EXPOSED AGGREGATE WORK

We are inclined to think that the various methods of producing decorative surfaces on concrete panels are recent developments. In many cases this is true, but some are merely refinements of methods that have been known for many years. For example, an article in the April 3, 1909 issue of *Engineering Record* describes in considerable detail methods of exposing surface aggregate in concrete to produce a decorative finish. Three different patents were granted previous to 1918 covering methods of achieving exposed aggregate surfaces.

An example of exposed aggregate concrete produced prior to 1920 is in Meridian Hill Park in Washington, D. C. (Fig. 1). This work was directed by John J. Earley. The close-up photograph, taken in 1961, reveals how well the surface appears after more than 40 years of exposure to the elements. By 1925, the Parthenon in Centennial Park, Nashville, Tenn., was completed with the exterior surfaces of exposed aggregate (Fig. 2). In 1932, Earley and his associates started work on panels and other precast units for one of the finest exposed aggregate

Fig. 1—Meridian Hill Park, Washington, D. C.

Fig. 2—Parthenon, Nashville, Tenn.

ACI member **T. W. Hunt,** decorative concrete specialist, Portland Cement Association, Chicago, is a member of ACI Committee 533, Precast Panels. A graduate of Missouri School of Mines, Rolla, he spent 20 years prior to joining the PCA staff with the Corps of Engineers.

Fig. 3—Baha'i Temple, Wilmette, Ill.

structures of all time—the Baha'i Temple, Wilmette, Ill. (Fig. 3). Because of shortage of building funds the exterior was not completed until early 1943. This building is an example of decorative concrete work which is still unsurpassed in detail and workmanship.

POST WORLD WAR II DEVELOPMENT

During the ten years following the end of World War II there was a steadily expanding use of precast panels, although this growth was not startling. Since 1955, however, there has been a tremendous increase in the use of precast concrete panels of all types, and a concurrent growth in the development of new textures and patterns. Reasons for this expanding usage include improved methods of production, better handling and erecting equipment, and development of new techniques and materials. Probably the greatest factor, however, has been the realization by architects that precast panels provide a pleasing variety of surface textures and patterns and exterior designs that generally cannot be accomplished as economically in other materials.

CHANGE IN PANEL SHAPE

For many years the typical panel was rectangular in shape, with a flat surface. Usually it was of only one color, such as white aggregate in a white cement matrix. Such panels still fill a large share of the requirements but the relative ease with which an almost unlimited range of shapes, designs, colors, and textures can be produced has stimulated the imagination of engineers and architects. Some idea of the variety of shapes that have been produced may be gained from a look at several new structures.

Fig. 4—Pan Am Building, New York, N. Y.

Fig. 5—Education Building, Wayne State University, Detroit, Mich.

Fig. 6—Maytag Company Office, Newton, Iowa

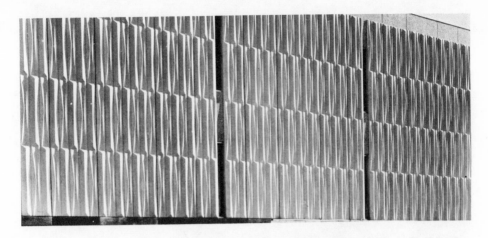

Fig. 7—Maytag Company Office, Newton, Iowa

Fig. 8—Garinger High School, Charlotte, N. C.

Fig. 9—Gimbels Store, Wauwatosa, Wis.

Fig. 10—Wachovia Bank & Trust Company,
Charlotte, N. C.

We have interesting panels on the exterior of the largest commercial office building, the Pan Am Building, located over Grand Central Station in New York (Fig. 4); the Education Building at Wayne State University in Detroit (Fig. 5); a new office building for the Maytag Company in Newton, Iowa (Fig. 6-7); a classroom building, part of a new high school complex (Fig. 8); a large department store near Milwaukee (Fig. 9); and a bank and office building in Charlotte, N. C. (Fig. 10).

GROWING USE OF COLOR

The increased use of color, both in the cement matrix and in exposed aggregate, has made it possible to produce patterns or designs in panel surfaces that add to their attractiveness. A few of the effects possible through combinations of two or more colors may be seen in the panels over the auditorium entrance at the Oak Park High School, Laurel, Miss. (Fig. 11); similar but larger panels enclose the Wieboldt Department Store in a Chicago shopping center (Fig. 12).

Fig. 11—Oak Park High School, Laurel, Miss.

Fig. 12—Wieboldt's Department Store, Chicago, Ill.

Fig. 13—Fremont Hotel, Las Vegas, Nev.

Fig. 14—Yates American Company, South Beloit, Ill.

It may be interesting to note that while these panels are rectangular in shape, by proper placement of the colored facing mixes it has been possible to create a harlequin diamond pattern. On the Wieboldt store there are nine panels to each bay, three wide by three high, with each panel being slightly under 8 x 14 ft. The L-shaped panels on the Fremont Hotel, Las Vegas, were designed to be distinctive even when surrounded by a jungle of signs and neon lights (Fig. 13).

A mural was made of 22 rectangular panels, each 6 x 14-1/2 ft., with a variety of colors being used to create an abstract representation of the products manufactured in a northern Illinois plant (Fig. 14). The designer deliberately developed a pattern that could be seen at a distance as the structure is set back from an Interstate highway with potential viewers traveling 70 mph.

DUAL PURPOSE PANELS

Another innovation has been the design of precast units to serve as both window frames and the exterior facade. When erected the units make up the entire wall surface, with no further additions. The precast exposed aggregate window frames that form the exterior of the new Bankers Trust Building (Fig. 15) on Park Avenue in New York are of white quartz aggregate in a white cement matrix with the glass being installed after the precast units had been

Fig. 16—City Hall, Phoenix, Ariz.

Fig. 15—Bankers Trust Company,
New York, N. Y.

Fig. 17—Hilton Hotel, Denver, Colo.

Fig. 18—500 Jefferson Building, Houston, Tex.

erected. Deeply recessed windows were provided in the frames that make up the exterior of the new Phoenix City Hall (Fig. 16), and the units on the Hilton Hotel in Denver (Fig. 17). Each unit on the hotel contains two windows. The 500 Jefferson Building (Fig. 18), erected in Houston during 1963, added a new fabrication technique to precast window unit production. The glass was installed at the precasting plant, eliminating glazing operations on this tall building. A secondary benefit of this method was that the precast units were handled a little more carefully with the glass in place.

STRUCTURAL PANELS AND UNITS

To date, practically all panels have been curtain wall units supported by the building frame. An occasional structure, however, has incorporated units that are both ornamental and structural. In some cases this has been done through the addition of an exposed aggregate surface to structural units, such as prestressed double-T members (Fig. 19). The John Hancock Insurance Building in Kansas City has a precast exterior frame of cross-shaped units with exposed aggregate surfaces on all sides (Fig. 20). This was accomplished by using white cement and white quartz aggregate in the mix and later exposing the aggregate by acid etching.

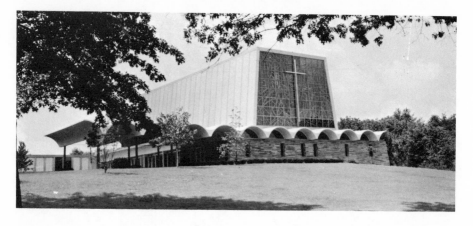

Fig. 19—Kenwood Baptist Church, Kenwood, Ohio

Fig. 20—John Hancock Life Insurance Co. Bldg., Kansas City, Mo.

Fig. 21—Police Administration Building, Philadelphia, Pa.

SHOCKED CONCRETE PROCESS

Several years ago, a new casting method was introduced to the panel industry in the United States under the name of "Schokbeton"—shocked concrete. The machinery used in this method was developed in Holland, and a number of franchised plants have since been established in this country. The process is mainly a means of consolidating a no-slump concrete mixture by raising and dropping the form about 1/4 in. some 250 times per minute. This contrasts with conventional methods of consolidation by means of high fre-

Fig. 22—Merchandise Mart, Atlanta, Ga.

Fig. 23—Library-Auditorium, Miami Beach, Fla.

quency and low amplitude vibration. Although the production of large precast panels by this method is relatively new, small concrete units have been produced in the past on so-called "drop tables" which followed the same technique without the refinement of modern machinery. The units for the new Police Administration Building (Fig. 21) in Philadelphia were manufactured from shocked concrete. These 5 x 25-ft panels not only have a fine appearance but are load-bearing structural panels that support the third and fourth floors and the roof load.

Fig. 24—Federal Science Building, Seattle, Wash.

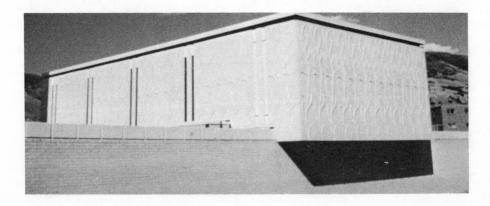

Fig. 25—University Stake House, Salt Lake City, Utah

Fig. 26—International Building, San Francisco, Calif.

MISCELLANEOUS PANEL TYPES

Sandwich panels have been used to some extent for many years. As we learn more about them, it seems likely that their usage will become more widespread. About 2000 sandwich units were used to inclose Atlanta's Merchandise Mart (Fig. 22).

Details and patterns may be sculptured in sand and later translated into precast panel surfaces to produce designs such as those seen on a portion of the Miami Beach Library (Fig. 23).

Although prestressing is not new to the field of precast decorative panels, it has been used rather infrequently in the past. It seems most likely that a greater use of prestressing of panels will occur in the future. Longer units may be cast and handled when prestressed. An example is the Federal Science Building at the Century 21 Exhibiton in Seattle where wall panels 55 ft long were used (Fig. 24).

SUMMARY

The great variety of textures, patterns, sizes and shapes that have been used on buildings from small one or two story structures (Fig. 25) to large multistory commercial office buildings (Fig. 26) may be considered just a beginning. There appears to be no limit to the variations that can be developed in this expanding and challenging field.

MATERIALS AND TESTS

Paper No. 2

A condensation of the deliberations of the ACI Committee 533 subcommittees on tests and materials, the paper concentrates on the desired properties of concrete for wall panels, such as durability, impermeability, and appearance, as affected by the various ingredients.

Precast Concrete Panels:
Materials and Tests

By J. A. Hanson and D. P. Jenny

■PRECAST CONCRETE WALL PANELS have been largely responsible for the accelerated use and evaluation of concrete as an esthetic, architectural material. Since these panels combine the many desirable and time-proven properties of concrete with emphasized beauty and function, it is imperative that the best materials and techniques available be used to achieve the desired effects. The added cost and care required for high quality will not materially affect the competitive advantage of concrete wall panels with respect to other materials and methods. On the other hand, the superior performance of quality panels will lead to increased demand by architects and owners.

The members of ACI Committee 533, Precast Wall Panels, have considered such a philosophy to be an implied but important adjunct to their assigned mission of development of recommendations for the design, manufacture, and erection of precast concrete wall panels. In order to accomplish this mission, the committee was divided into six subcommittees with varying areas of interest. Duplication of the material considered in these subcommittees cannot be completely eliminated. Indeed, it would be most difficult to clearly separate the work of the subcommittee on materials and that of the subcommittee on tests. Consequently, this paper is a combination of the deliberations of these two subcommittees. Most of the discussion has been concentrated in the area of materials for concrete wall panels because the subcommittee on tests has published a progress report.*

---

*This report is reprinted in the appendix to this volume.

A quick appraisal of precast concrete wall panels discloses this general listing of materials involved in their manufacture:

1. Concrete—and all its ingredients.
2. Reinforcement, inserts, and miscellaneous metal.
3. Insulating materials.
4. Forming materials.

To this might be added the additional categories involved in installation:

5. Jointing materials.
6. Protective coatings.

This report will deal principally with concrete since the second and third items involve panel design, the fourth is tied to fabrication and its many techniques, and the remaining two items concern erection and installation, all subjects of other subcommittee reports. However, comments will be offered on all material groupings.

CONCRETE

Cement

For precast concrete panels, a white or gray portland cement meeting the requirements of Types I, IA, III, or IIIA as specified in ASTM C150, ASTM C175, or Federation Specification SS-C-192 should be used. Other cement types are not considered necessary in precast work.

Cement of the same type and brand and from the same mill should be used for the panels on a given project to minimize color variations. Some precasters prefer to obtain a single, one-time shipment for a given project. However, these precautions alone will not automatically assure color uniformity because variables in panel manufacture may also have marked effects.

Samples provided to architects should be keyed or coded to the type, brand, and source of cement used, as well as to the facing aggregates and other materials.

Aggregate

Although much of the recent development in precast concrete panels has been in the decorative exposed aggregate curtain walls, there is still a place for the unfaced panels, either plain, patterned, or textured. The concrete used in these and in the back-up concrete for the faced panels, should, of course, be uniform, high-quality, controlled concrete in order to obtain desirable properties and performance in the panels.

ACI member, **J. A. Hanson**, manager, Products and Applications Section, Portland Cement Association Research and Development Laboratories, Skokie, Ill., is chairman of ACI Committee 213, Lightweight Aggregates and Lightweight Aggregate Concrete, and a member of 533, Precast Panels, and 435, Deflection of Concrete Building Structures.

ACI member **Daniel P. Jenny**, chief engineer, Expanded Shale, Clay and Slate Institute, Washington, D. C., is a member of four ACI Committees: 213, Lightweight Aggregates and Lightweight Aggregate Concrete; 408, Bond Stress; 531, Concrete Masonry Structures; and 533, Precast Panels.

For this type of concrete, normal weight aggregates conforming to ASTM C33 and lightweight structural aggregates meeting the requirements of ASTM C330 should be used. Maximum aggregate size is rarely greater than 3/4 in., sometimes being 1/2 in. or smaller for thin panels. This top size is an important factor in proportioning concrete. For example, optimum air contents* for both normal weight and lightweight concrete should be in accordance with Table 1.

In addition, percentage of fine aggregate to total aggregate increases as the top size of aggregate decreases.

TABLE 1—OPTIMUM AIR CONTENT

3/4 in. maximum size aggregate . . . . 6 ± 1-1/2 percent air
1/2 in. maximum size aggregate . . . . 7 ± 1-1/2 percent air
3/8 in. maximum size aggregate . . . . 8 ± 1-1/2 percent air
1/4 in. maximum size aggregate . . . . 9 ± 1-1/2 percent air

Back up concrete

This classification of concrete is also meant to include the concrete in unfaced panels.

Compressive strength is not necessarily the primary concrete property sought in panel work. Durability, impermeability, and appearance are generally more important. However, to assure these desirable properties, compressive strengths of 4000 psi or greater are recommended. High strengths are particularly important for back-up concrete since it should have aggregate to cement proportions similar to that of the high strength, exposed aggregate facing concrete, to minimize effects of differential properties. It also has significance for concrete panels that are textured by bush-hammering or sand blasting. On these the broken or open surface may lead to excessive absorption and increased permeability if low strength concrete were permitted.

As a guide for initial trial mixes to obtain concretes which will meet the above requirements, Table 2 presents suggested cement contents, aggregate percentages and water-cement ratios.

Strength tests

Standard 6 x 12-in. test cylinders for compressive strength tests should be taken whenever practicable. If low slump or zero-slump concrete is used in making the panels, internal or external vibration on the test cylinders is recommended in accordance with ASTM C31 and C192.

For a number of reasons, it may be more advantageous or desirable to perform compressive tests on cubes that are either cast or sawn. Committee 533 recommends a standard 4-in. cube with a correction factor of 0.8.

$$f_c'{}_{CUBE} \times 0.80 = f_c'{}_{CYLINDER}$$

Both values should be reported. A 4-in. cube accommodates a maximum aggregate size of 1-1/2 in. without excessive test deviations.

In addition to strength tests for compliance with specifications, it is recom-

---

*These air contents do not apply to the special facing mixes.

mended that producers institute day-to-day tests and maintain continuous records for quality control and demonstration purposes.

Facing aggregates

By far the most exciting development in precast concrete panels involves the myriad combinations of special aggregates exposed in the panel face for their color and texture. Such aggregates include selected gravels, limestone, quartz, marble, granite, glass, and ceramics. The precaster should be certain that all aggregates come from the same source and are of the same quality and color as the approved sample.

Because of the relatively higher cost of these aggregates, they are most generally mixed in a facing concrete which is backed up with concrete using regular aggregates. The facing layer need only be thick enough to prevent the back-up concrete from showing. Usually gap gradation is desirable to emphasize a certain size and lead to more uniformity of coverage with this particle size. Maximum size may vary from 5-in. cobbles to No. 4 sand, but the usual range is from 1-1/4 to 3/8 in. Materials, colors, gradations, size, and reveal are the variables that permit extreme freedom of architectural expression; hence, the only limits should be those of judgment based on experience or trial.

At no time should soft, nondurable aggregates be permitted for exposed aggregate work. Certain limestones and marbles may fall in this category, therefore proven performance records should accompany all facing aggregates.

Generally, panel precasters use facing aggregates that have previous service records and hence alkali reactivity is rarely, if ever, encountered. Tests for the potential alkali reactivity should be made on any new combination of aggregate and cement. This is best done by expansion measurements on mortar bars prepared and tested in accordance with ASTM C227. The coarse aggregate is

TABLE 2—GUIDE FOR INITIAL TRIAL MIXES

Compressive strength, psi	Maximum size aggregate, in.	Lightweight concrete*		Normal weight concrete*		Maximum water-cement ratio
		Cement content, 94–lb bags per cu yd	Fine aggregate, percent of total vol.	Cement content, 94–lb bags per cu yd	Fine aggregate, percent of total vol.	
4000	1/4	7.25	100	6.5	100	6.5 U.S. gal. per 94-lb bag (0.576 by weight)
	3/8	7.00	60-70	6.1	42-50	
	1/2	6.75	55-65	5.8	39-47	
	3/4	6.50	50-60	5.5	36-44	
5000	1/4	8.25	100	8.00	100	5.5 U.S. gal. per 94-lb bag (0.488 by weight)
	3/8	8.00	60-70	7.75	36-44	
	1/2	7.75	55-65	7.50	34-42	
	3/4	7.50	45-60	7.25	32-40	

*The slump of lightweight concrete in this guide is 1 to 3 in.—approximately 2 in. less than the slump of normal weight concrete at equal workability. If panel complexity should require slumps greater than 3 in., cement contents should be correspondingly increased to maintain strength.

crushed, sieved, and recombined for making the mortar. The limits of expansion should not exceed that given in ASTM C33. If the limits are exceeded it is recommended that a low alkali cement (a maximum of 0.6 percent expressed as Na_2O equivalent) be used with that aggregate or that a different aggregate be selected.

Glass aggregate is used for bright colors. This material should be specifically formulated so that is is nonreactive with portland cement.

Once in a while, coarse facing aggregates may contain particles with an iron content that results in unsightly stains. Such material would undoubtedly meet the staining requirements for ordinary plastic concrete, thus other tests or methods must be devised to eliminate this occasional trouble. Selectivity on the part of the precaster and his experience with materials and sources is currently the only assurance against iron stains from aggregate.

Facing concrete

Panels are almost always cast in a horizontal position to permit a number of different techniques to be used to gain satisfactory exposed aggregate finishes. In one method, aggregate may be spread or placed on the forms and covered or coated with a sand-cement grout using either white or gray portland cement or a pigmented matrix. In another, special aggregates may be applied to top surfaces of horizontally-cast panels. Generally, a thin layer of facing concrete containing the special surface aggregates is placed in the forms initially and then backed with regular concrete. Sometimes the facing mix is placed on the top surface and additional aggregate worked in if necessary.

Usually facing mixes with a high aggregate concentration and gap gradation are rather harsh and are mixed to a slump of 4 to 6 in. to achieve workability. By using a dry back-up mix, excess water can be drawn from the facing concrete, thus improving its quality. A measure of this improved strength may be obtained by fabricating 4 x 4 x 8-in. prisms, consisting of 4 in. of facing mix and 4 in. of back-up concrete, cast in a manner similar to the panels. After sawing the prism in half, each concrete may be tested on the resulting 4-in. cubes.

In other techniques, high cement content, low slump, and heavy vibration are combined to give facing mix strengths of 9000 to 10,000 psi and even more. When testing mixes of this type for compressive strength, special high strength capping materials should be used or the bearing surfaces should be lapped to a plane surface.

Minimum strength of facing mixes should be 5000 psi. Furthermore, cement content of facing mixes should not be less than 6 bags per cu yd, or the equivalent in cementitious materials, to assure maximum density and minimum permeability.

In all facing concrete, air entrainment is recommended. However, because of the characteristics of these mixes, a specified percentage of air often is not practical. Instead, use of air-entraining cements or air-entraining agents in amounts equal to "normal" dosage is recommended. Normal dosage results in 19 ± 3 percent in a 1:4 standard sand mortar tested in accordance with ASTM C185.

Durability tests

Because of the orientation of precast wall panels in structures and because of the high strength, low permeability characteristics of the exposed concrete, the coincidence of high degrees of saturation with severe freezing is almost non-existent. Thus excellent durability can be expected and performance and tests bear this out. Hence, it is recommended that specifications do not require freeze-thaw durability tests but do include, at all times, air-entrainment requirements.

There are certain exceptions to this general statement, such as panels located at sidewalk level, where durability tests may be considered necessary. In these instances, the reasonably realistic testing cycle of freezing and thawing in air with water flushing of the surface just prior to each freezing cycle is recommended.

Absorption tests

Tests have never adequately shown that absorption test limits on concrete are a measure of durability. Furthermore, the vertical orientation and the concrete quality are factors that make it difficult for a panel in service to reach the actual absorption condition as obtained in an absorption test. Thus, an absorption test is not recommended as a control for durability.

Absorption tests, such as ASTM C97, might be adopted by a precaster to serve as a relative measure of the ability of different concretes to resist dirt adherence and of possible staining from aggregates, fading of colors, or other factors leading to nonuniform appearance or unsightliness. At best, any absorption test is only an indicator.

Admixtures

Generally, only air-entraining admixtures conforming to ASTM C260 are used in precast panel work. Accelerating admixtures may be used for rapid strength gain. However, the general practice is not to use an accelerator but to use a Type III cement plus a curing method that leads to high early strengths needed for early form removal. Water reducing admixtures may provide benefits by reducing the amount of water for workability and by minimizing detrimental bleeding of excess water. These may find a place particularly in the harsh facing mixes with their necessarily poor aggregate gradation. Care should be exercised that the particular formulation of the water reducing admixture is not combined with retarding characteristics, or if so, that this fact be known and the retarding effects be evaluated.

Retarding admixtures generally have no place in precast concrete panel work. A retarded concrete may not permit the top surfaces of a panel to be finished off or textured rapidly enough to fit the high speed casting cycles generally found in plant production. Also, a few tests have indicated a greater tendency toward efflorescence with some retarders, especially when panels receive accelerated curing. On the other hand, retarding admixtures will increase the efficiency and uniformity of aggregate exposure when using surface retardation. Surface retardants for aggregate reveal are discussed in the section under formwork.

Pigments

To augment the architecture of concrete panels, color tints in the matrix may be obtained through the use of pigments. Pigments commonly used for this purpose are finely ground natural or synthetic mineral oxides. Synthetic oxides are perhaps more satisfactory from the standpoint of more attractive shades and greater permanence.

Iron oxides produce shades of yellow, buff, tan, brown, maroon, red, and black. Chromium oxide produces green and cobalt oxide, blue. Variable amounts of these materials, expressed as a percentage of the cement content by weight, produce various shades of these colors. Amounts in excess of 5 percent seldom accomplish further color intensity. Pigments used with white cement will produce clearer shades than with gray. It is good practice to blend the pigment with the cement in the dry state prior to mixing.

Recently, organic, phthalocyanine dyes have been used successfully in concrete to produce light to dark shades of blue and green. Their service record is, of necessity, quite short. While their initial cost is quite high, they are used in small quantities of less than 1 percent by weight of cement. As a further advantage, they can be dispersed in the mix water, thus eliminating the need for preblending.

In the use of any coloring agent it is important to have tests or performance records that reliably indicate their color stability in concrete. Furthermore, it should be realized that concrete colored by pigments, as well as with colored aggregates, may weather to some degree so that the panel's color intensity may be dulled in time.

REINFORCEMENT

The type and quality of reinforcement for concrete panels will depend on the size and function of the wall panels. Dimensions vary so widely that all sizes and kinds of reinforcement common to general concrete construction may be used. These include structural, intermediate, and high strength deformed bars, high-tensile rods and strands for prestressing purposes, and black or galvanized welded wire fabric with a wide variety of mesh spacings and wire gages. A recent development has been the production of mesh with deformed wire.

The requirements for thin wall panels are closely allied to those of "Minimum Requirements for Thin-Section Precast Concrete Construction (ACI 525-63)," which allows a minimum cover of 3/8-in. and requires the use of 2 x 2-in. mesh for elements with a section thickness of 3-in. or less. For this minimum cover, galvanized mesh is desirable; for covers of 3/4 in. or more, galvanized reinforcement is not necessary, although many precasters prefer its use.

Three-layer sandwich panel construction requires concrete ribs or metal shear ties to connect the outer structural concrete wythes. The metal ties are often fabricated of expanded metal or of various truss-type products produced commercially for masonry reinforcement or building studding. Metal shear ties should incorporate diagonal members for proper resistance to horizontal shearing deformation in sandwich panels.

INSULATING MATERIALS

The highly insulative sandwich wall panel involves a design compromise between high resistance to heat transfer, economy, and structural requirements such as strength, weight, bond, and stiffness. A wide variety of sandwich materials are available to provide the desirable thermal properties. Since conductivity, a measure of heat flow, varies with density, unit weight may be used to classify these insulating materials.

Under 15 lb per cu ft

Plastic materials—Polyurethane foam (boards or granules), polystyrene foam (boards or granules).

Glass materials—Foamed glass (boards or granules), glass fiber (batts).

Paper honey-comb—Usually filled with insulating granules or aggregate.

15 to 50 lb per cu ft

Foamed concrete—Autoclaved cellular concrete (boards), nonautoclaved cellular concrete (boards or plastic fill).

Mineral aggregate concrete—Vermiculite (boards or plastic fill), perlite (boards or plastic fill).

Some of the prefabricated concrete insulating materials may have high initial rates of absorption. In sandwich panel construction, these materials are placed in direct contact with the plastic concrete faces and over-dessication of the fresh concrete may occur to the extent that cement would not properly hydrate. These insulation materials should have a water repellant coating which does not hinder bond and which prevents accumulation of moisture, thereby maintaining their high insulation value.

FORMING MATERIALS

Structural formwork

Good forms are vitally important in precast panel work and the type depends on considerations of cost, maintenance, re-use, and detail, and possibly salvage.

Concrete, wood, and steel forms are quite common. Polyester resins reinforced with glass fiber are finding more and more applications. For complicated details, molds of plaster, gelatine, or sculptured sand have been used successfully and, depending on the size of the cast, these molds are often combined or reinforced with wooden forms.

Liners

Patterns and textures, that range from muted expression to bold relief, are obtained with different types of liners.

Rubber matting is effective and the concrete faithfully reproduces the most complicated surfaces. Commercial material is generally satisfactory but it should be tried beforehand, especially if pigments are used, to determine whether staining or discoloration results. Trials will also determine the best time for stripping so that the surface remains intact and the liners can be re-used.

Wood, either as boards, plywood panels, or nailed-on inserts, works well. Liner surfaces should be sealed with shellac and then lightly coated with form oil prior to casting.

Pleasing and unusual architectural effects in concrete can be obtained by the use of forms made of plastics. The plastic sheets used for this purpose may be vacuum-formed to provide bold or muted patterns to an extent limited only by the architect's imagination. The concrete surfaces can be either glossy-smooth or textured. In either case, no parting agents and no subsequent treatment to the concrete surfaces are required. The extremely fine finish of plastic formed concrete greatly enhances the attractiveness of integral colors and, because of high reflectivity, smaller amounts of pigment are required to obtain a given color intensity. The glossy surfaced concrete, while performing in an excellent manner for indoor decoration, is not recommended for exterior exposure by reason of gradual and nonuniform disappearance of its reflectivity. For outdoor exposure it is recommended that either textured surfaces or smooth but nonglossy surfaces, achieved through early form removal, be used.

Polyethylene film laid over uniformly distributed cobblestones provides dimpled surfaces. Pieces of polystyrene foam, shaped and attached to the form, impart deeply impressed designs after removal from the concrete face.

Retarders

When exposed aggregate panels are cast face down, it is quite common to use commercially available chemical retarders on the form to achieve the required reveal of the special facing aggregates. These retarders generally consist of various hydroxylated organic compounds and may be either organic solvent or water soluble. Most suppliers provide several grades depending on the depth of reveal desired. For 3/8-in. aggregates, exposures to depths of 1/16 or 1/8 in. are practical, and for aggregates up to 3/4 in., the etch may be increased to 1/4 in. although generally it is somewhat less. Light or medium grade retarders are employed for these aggregate sizes and, in the case of flat forms, a retarder-impregnated cloth has been used quite successfully. For aggregates larger than 3/4 in., the desired reveal may be considerably greater, and a retarder in gel form is available for this purpose. Care should be taken to insure uniform application of the gel to the structural form. For the exposure of aggregates of 1/4-in. size or smaller it may be better practice to use methods other than chemical retarders.

Many factors affect the optimum time interval when the panels should be removed from the forms and the retarded paste brushed and washed away. Since the most suitable time may vary from 12 to 24 hr after casting, preliminary tests should be performed before setting up the casting cycles for a large contract.

After aggregate is properly exposed, and the panel is well cured, a mild acid wash of 5 to 10 percent muriatic acid will clean and brighten the colored aggregate. Immediately thereafter the panel should be thoroughly flushed.

JOINTING MATERIALS

Joint sealants may be classified into three general categories: (1) cement mortars, (2) mastics, primarily oleo-resinous (oil base) caulking compounds, and (3) thermosetting plastics including polysulfides and epoxy resins. Of these, only the mastics and thermosetting plastics should be used as sealants in precast concrete panel installations. Cement mortars are not extensible and cannot accommodate the movement of the larger panels.

The oleo-resinous (oil-base) compounds vary in performance depending on brand and formulation but even the best dry out in time and must be renewed. The service life of the better materials may be in excess of 5 years with an occasional instance of satisfactory performance considerably longer.

Polysulfide sealants are usually two-part compounds, and they are more expensive than oil-base caulking materials. The higher initial cost is more than offset by lower maintenance costs and assurance of weather-tight joints. Proper formulation and proper installation of polysulfide sealants result in good adhesion, flexibility, and durability.

It is desirable to use the minimum amount of sealant required to make a satisfactory joint. Not only is it more economical, but it results in better sealant life as a relatively thin band of material is less likely to fail than a thick section of sealant. It is good practice to fill most of the joint space with some type of premolded elastic material and to use the sealant only in the exterior 1/2-in. portions of the joint. A variety of materials are available for use as joint fillers including sponge rubber; polyvinyl chloride; and foamed polyethylene, polyurethane, and polystyrene. The foamed or sponge materials should be compressed to about one-half their unrestrained thickness when they are installed so that they will continue to fill the joint should contraction of the panel widen the joints. The polysulfide sealant should be installed to a depth of about one-half the width of the joint, but not exceeding 1/2 in.

Good workmanship by qualified sealant applicators is the biggest factor leading to satisfactory performance. The American Standards Association has adopted a standard specification: "Polysulfide-Base Sealing Compounds for the Building Trade," ASA A116.1-1960.

PROTECTIVE COATINGS

Protective coatings, primarily clear silicones, remain an area of controversy among panel manufacturers. Some feel their water repellant properties prevent discoloration and keep colors bright. Others, are concerned that the benefits are overrated and that possible harmful effects, such as surface spalling, may occur under certain conditions. Tests have shown that these water repellants do not improve resistance to frost action and that this property is best achieved in the concrete by means of air-entrainment. Furthermore, it is difficult to repair the face of a panel that has already received a silicone coating. However, it is generally agreed that panels coated with silicones are much easier to clean.

When coatings are used, their behavior should be based on prior experience under similar exposure conditions. Care should be exercised to apply in the manner and the coverages recommended by the manufacturer and also to prevent accidental application on those surfaces that will be in contact with joint sealants. It should be recognized that silicones have a limited useful life and need renewal from time to time.

DESIGN TRENDS AND STANDARDS

Reviews design analyses, standards of practice, and details of precast concrete wall panels as they pertain to specific applications. Suggests a recommended practice for the design of precast wall panels.

Precast Concrete Wall Panels: Design Trends and Standards

By Victor F. Leabu

■THE EVOLUTIONARY PROCESS in the development and use of precast concrete for wall panels has been phenomenal in all phases of design, construction, and to some extent, standardization. However, a standardization of design practice or a recommended design guide has yet to be developed for this unique type of construction material.

Many unusual, unique designs and methods of construction of precast concrete wall panels have been successfully executed in the past, and are in constant development today. The structural integrity, safety, feasibility, and economy of the many types of precast wall panels developed in the past two decades have depended to a great extent on the skill and judgment of the architect and engineer, and to the success and capability of the precast concrete industry in the execution of the plans and specifications of these elements in the field. In many cases, only past experience and experimentation have been the key to the design standard used for future development of the precast wall panels.

The precast concrete wall panel has evolved from the heavy piece of flat, gray concrete used to enclose the secondary type of building or warehouse structure, to the imposing elegant aggregate surface precast curtain walls of exotic shapes. This rapid development has instituted the need for some kind of standard, design, or recommended practice for continued progress in the precast wall panel field and has been the motivating force in organizing ACI Committee 533, Precast Panels.

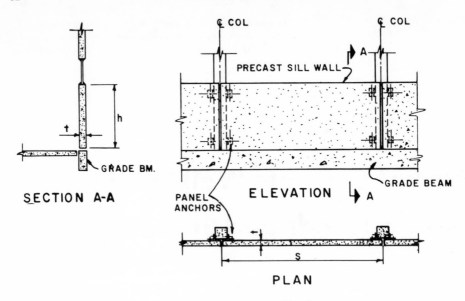

Fig. 1—Precast concrete sill wall

The first precast wall panels were 8 to 10 in. thick solid concrete averaging 8 to 10 ft wide by 20 to 30 ft long and used as sill or closure walls (Fig. 1). These panels were generally fabricated on the site and in many cases, tilted into position. This type of precast wall panel is usually designed using the provisions of the current ACI Building Code. The panel is considered as a reinforced concrete wall with the exception of being precast instead of cast-in-place. Critical design conditions during fabrication and erection are considered in the design.

Precast sandwich panel

The development of the precast sandwich panel, approximately 20 years ago, gave spectacular rise to the use of the precast wall panel. These panels, 4 to 6 in. thick, consist of an insulation core (such as foam glass, glass fiber, or expanded polystyrene or polyurethane) sandwiched between two layers of normal weight or lightweight concrete (Fig. 2 and 3). These lightweight members provided the construction industry with a precast concrete panel that could compete with the thin-metal curtain wall in weight, cost, and insulation efficiency.

As a result of this development, precast concrete panels, which were previously used as sill walls supported on grade beams and spanning between columns or isolated footings, could now be suspended between columns as

ACI member **Victor F. Leabu,** chief structural engineer, Giffels and Rossetti, Inc., Detroit, is a member of ACI Committee 533, Precast Panels, and 347, Formwork for Concrete. He is a graduate of the University of Michigan and is a registered professional engineer.

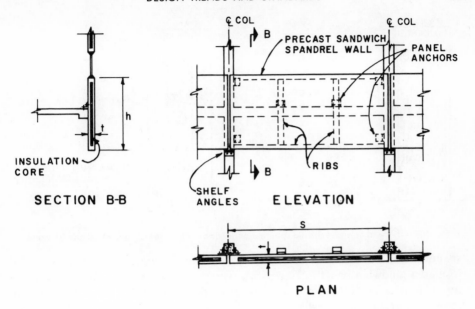

Fig. 2—Precast concrete spandrel wall

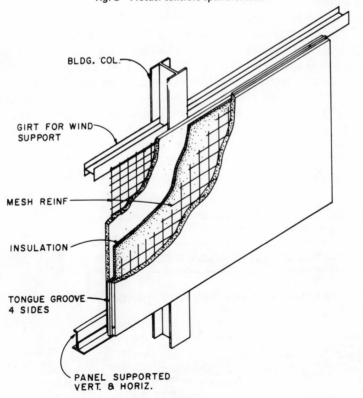

Fig. 3—Typical sandwich wall construction supported on structural frame

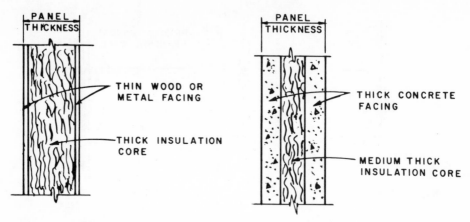

Fig. 4—(left) Wood or metal curtain spandrel panel and (right) precast concrete sandwich panel

spandrel walls or spanned vertically from floor to floor. In many cases, the insulated sandwich panel is used as a closure curtain wall, tongue and grooved on all four sides and supported vertically and horizontally by a concrete or steel structural framing system.

A satisfactory standard for the design of sandwich or insulated precast wall panels has yet to be developed. In contrast to the metal or wood sandwich panel, the precast concrete sandwich panel has a high ratio of skin area to insulation core area ranging from 1 to 3. This ratio for the metal or wood sandwich panel is usually between 0.1 to 0.5 (Fig. 4). The degree of composite action of the concrete layers and the variety of insulation cores used in this type of panel is reported elsewhere in this symposium, but the ability of the wall panel to resist bending and compressive loads may still require further investigation and research. Most wall panels of the sandwich type are being developed on the basis of past experience and engineering practice.

In a sandwich panel, the most desirable action of the panel under load is as an integral single unit with the full thickness always effective. Composite

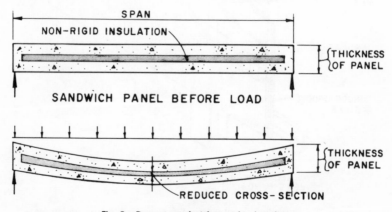

Fig. 5—Precast sandwich panel in bending

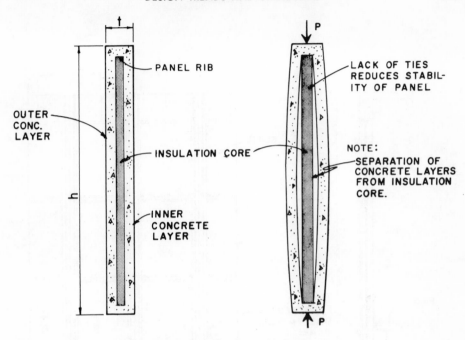

Fig. 6—Precast sandwich panel in compression

action of the sandwich panel depends to a great extent on the type of insulation core (rigid and nonrigid) used, the thickness of the concrete layers, and the use and spacing of concrete ribs and mechanical shear ties. The lack of composite stability due to insufficient ribs, mechanical shear ties between the concrete layers, and the use of nonrigid insulation core, reduces the effective cross section and the load carrying capacity of the precast wall panel in shear, bending, or compression (Fig. 5 and 6).

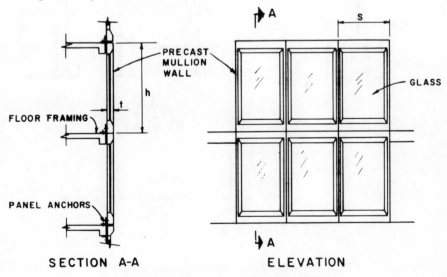

SECTION A-A   ELEVATION

Fig. 7—Window type mullion wall panel

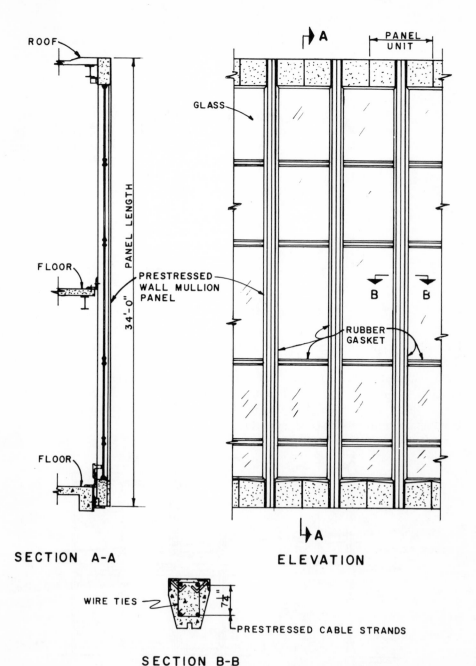

ROOF

GLASS

FLOOR

PANEL LENGTH

34'-0"

PRESTRESSED
WALL MULLION
PANEL

FLOOR

SECTION A-A

PANEL
UNIT

A

B   B

RUBBER
GASKET

A

ELEVATION

WIRE TIES

7¼"

PRESTRESSED CABLE STRANDS

SECTION B-B

Fig. 8—Precast prestressed concrete mullion type wall

Special type panels

More recent developments of precast concrete wall panels have involved the use of a variety of surface treatments, such as exposed aggregates, mosaic, glass and marble chips, as well as textured and smooth surface finishes that are obtained by the application of industrial techniques developed in the precast industry.

A variety of shapes limited only by the imagination of the architect and designer have become popular in the field of precast wall panels in the past 6 years. The window-type mullion wall panel, with or without integral surface facing, is common in the curtain walls used on many highrise structures being built today. In many cases, this type of precast wall panel is replacing the metal curtain wall, not only on the basis of esthetics, but also on the basis of economy (Fig. 7 and 8). In many cases, the designer now has a material that can be molded in any conceivable shape made possible only in precast concrete.

Prestressed panels

Many variations of the mullion-type panel are now being used. In many cases, the precast sections have been developed on relatively thin cross sections by the use of prestressed concrete. The use of prestressing, both post-tensioning and pretensioning, has made the handling and erection of large precast units as well as thin sections possible without cracking or overstressing due to service loads (Fig. 8).

SUGGESTED PRELIMINARY DESIGN RECOMMENDATIONS FOR PRECAST WALL PANELS

To cover the many variations and unlimited types, shapes and configurations of precast wall panel units in a design standard would be impossible within the scope of this paper. Therefore, the following suggested preliminary design recommendation is intended as a guide, a general reference and as a beginning to the more important aspects of precast wall panel design. Continued effort of ACI Committee 533, Precast Panels, will no doubt, refine and further develop this recommendation for formal presentation to the Institute as a recommended practice for precast wall panels for the use of the designing engineer and the precast industry.

Scope and limitations

The following suggested minimum design recommendations for precast wall panels are preliminary in development and do not include all the design criteria and formulas required for precast panels. Materials, tests, fabrication, tolerances or erection standards are not included. These sections are in the process of development by other subcommittees of ACI Committee 533.

The design recommendations cover only the types of precast construction used as precast wall panels. This includes wall panels of solid, ribbed, cored or sandwich-type of construction (Fig. 9) cast from normal weight or light-

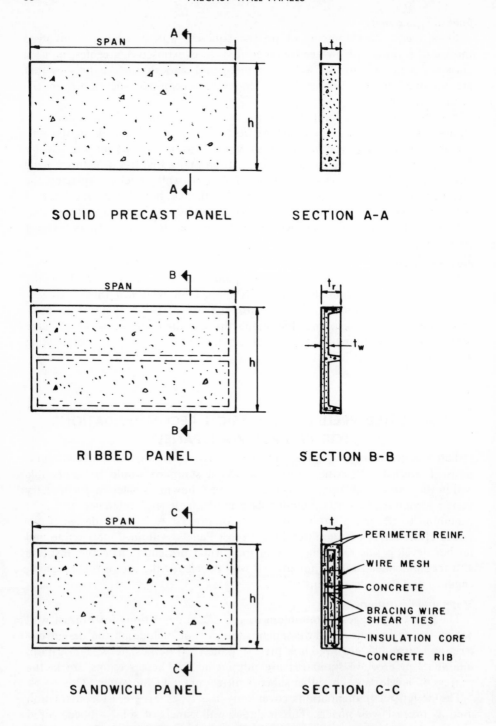

Fig. 9—Solid, ribbed, and sandwich type precast concrete wall panels

weight concrete with or without integral surface facing. Prestressed wall panels are also included in this standard.

These minimum design requirements for precast wall panels are to be used in connection with "Building Code Requirements for Reinforced Concrete (ACI 318-63)."

Applicable codes, standards, and recommendations

All references to codes, specifications, recommended practices and standards listed or appearing in the design recommendations, are applicable:

"Building Code Requirements for Reinforced Concrete (ACI 318-63)."

"Specification for the Design, Fabrication and Erection of Structural Steel for Building (AISC 1961)" and "Specification for Architecturally Exposed Structural Steel (AISC 1960)."

"Aluminum Construction Manual," Aluminum Association (1959).

"Recommended Practices for Welding Reinforcing Steel Metal Inserts and Connections in Reinforced Concrete Construction (AWS D12.1-61)."

"Manual of Standard Practice for Detailing Reinforced Concrete Structures (ACI 315-65)."

Applicable ASTM specifications covering material used in precast concrete.

"Minimum Requirements for Thin-Section Precast Concrete Construction (ACI 525-63)."

All recommended standards and practices not listed above, but included in other sections of the ACI Committee 533 report are part of this recommendation.

Design methods

The design of the precast wall panels should be made either with reference to allowable working stresses, service loads, and the accepted straight line theory of flexure (working stress design) or with reference to load factors and strengths (ultimate strength design) as given in ACI 318-63.

The control of construction should be consistent with the design method selected by the engineer and approved by the local building codes.

Design loads

The provisions for the design herein specified are based on the assumption that all precast wall panels will be designed for all the dead and live loads carried by the panels and that the live loads will be in accordance with the general requirements of applicable local building codes pertaining to this type of construction.

1. Where precast wall panels are used as load bearing walls or story columns, load reductions for multiple stories will be permitted.

2. Where wall panels are used to resist wind and/or seismic forces, these forces should be determined in accordance with recognized methods and/or by the local codes and should be combined with the effects of dead and live loads carried by the precast wall units.

3. Wall panels and connections designed to resist wind should be designed for equal positive and negative pressures and if located in seismic areas, for

earthquake forces acting in any horizontal direction including torsional forces resulting from seismic loads.

4. The effects of forces due to concrete shrinkage, temperature differential, creep, prestressing, handling and erection loads, and *eccentric* loads should be considered in the design where required and as given by ACI 318-63.

Design stresses

Notation—

A_b = Bearing area of precast wall panel in contact with supporting frame (sq in.).

A_c = Maximum area of supporting member that is geometrically similar to and concentric with the bearing area of the precast wall unit (sq in.).

E_c = Modulus of elasticity of concrete as given in ACI 318-63.

F_a = Allowable direct compressive stress (psi).

f_a = Computed direct compressive stress (psi).

F_b = Allowable maximum bending stress (psi) for panels loaded normal to face of panel.

f_b = Computed bending stress (psi) for panels loaded normal to face of panel.

F_{br} = Allowable maximum bearing stress (psi).

F_c = Allowable compressive stress (psi) in flexure for panels used as beams and loaded in plane of panel.

f_c = Computed compressive stress (psi) for panels used as beams and loaded in plane of panel.

f_c' = Specified compressive strength of concrete at 28 days or at earlier age as determined by cylinder test (psi).

h

or = Height or distance (span) between supports (in.).

l

t_e = Effective thickness of precast wall (in.).

Allowable design stresses in normal weight and lightweight concrete and for reinforcing and prestressing steel should conform to the requirements of ACI 318-63.

Specific allowable design stresses pertaining to wall panels are included for reference. Panels should conform to the requirements of ACI 318-63, except as herein noted.

Precast wall panels used as bearing walls or columns loaded in plane of panel—The allowable direct compressive stress in the concrete for concentric loads, based on working stress design, should not exceed the following for normal weight concrete:

$$F_a = 0.2f_c' \left[1 - \left(\frac{h}{40\ t_e}\right)^3\right]$$

The above equation is plotted for f_c' = 3000, 4000, and 5000 psi in Fig. 10. When the reinforcement in the bearing wall is designed, placed, and anchored in position as for tied columns, the allowable stresses shall be those for tied columns in which the ratio of vertical reinforcement should not exceed 0.04. For concentrated loads, the length of the wall to be considered as effective for each should not exceed the center to center dimensions between loads nor should it exceed the width of the bearing plus four times the wall thickness.

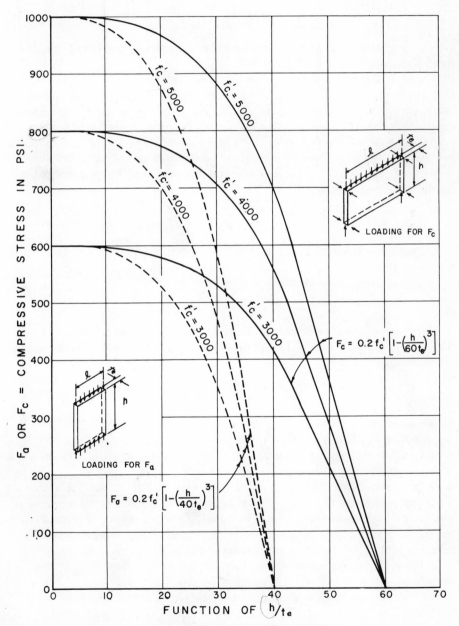

Fig. 10—Recommended allowable compressive stress for precast concrete panels based on h/t_e ratios

Precast wall panels used as beams loaded in the plane of the panel—Allowable compressive stress in concrete for precast concrete walls which span horizontally as deep beams between columns, supports or isolated footings, should not exceed the following for normal weight concrete:

$$F_c = 0.2f_c' \left[1 - \left(\frac{l}{60\,t_e}\right)^3\right]$$

Where height of panel $h \leq 8$ ft. The above equation is plotted for $f_c' = 3000$, 4000, and 5000 psi in Fig. 10.

Precast wall panels used as beams or slabs loaded normal to panel—Allowable compressive stress in concrete for precast panels which span vertically, horizontally or as a two-way slab should be as per ACI 318-63 considering the proper effective sections for the solid, ribbed, cored, or sandwich panels.

Precast wall panels controlled by compression and designed for combined compressive stresses—These panels should meet the following requirements:

1. Panels subjected to direct loads and bending about one principal axis should be so proportioned that

$$\frac{f_a}{F_a} + \frac{f_b}{F_b} \leq 1$$

2. Panels subjected to bending about two principal axes should be so proportioned that

$$\frac{f_c}{F_c} + \frac{f_b}{F_b} \leq 1$$

Maximum bearing pressures—Maximum bearing pressures under precast wall panels (i.e. on area A_b), supported on steel or concrete frame should not exceed the following:

$$F_{br} = 0.4f_c' \sqrt[3]{A_c/A_b} \leq f_c'$$

Effective section

Solid panels—

1. In solid concrete panels without a surface facing, the effective thickness of the concrete panel should be the full thickness.

2. In solid concrete panels monolithically cast with a surface facing having a compressive strength equal to or greater than the concrete back-up of the panel, the effective thickness should be equal to the panel total thickness minus the depth of the reveal of the exposed aggregate surface where the depth of reveal exceeds 3 percent of the total panel thickness.

3. In solid concrete panels that have a separate facing that is not cast monolithically with the panel, the effective structural thickness of the panel should be the total panel thickness minus the separate facing thickness.

Ribbed panels—

1. In ribbed or T-beam construction of wall panels, the flange and stem should be built monolithically for effective integral action.

2. The effective flange width to be used in the design of symetrical ribbed panels or T-beams should not exceed one-fourth of the span length of the wall panel. The overhanging width of the flange on either side of the stem should not exceed eight times the thickness of the flange nor one-half the clear distance to the next stem.

3. For wall panels having a flange on one side only, the effective overhanging flange width should not exceed one-twelfth of the span length of the wall panel, nor six times the thickness of the flange nor one-half the clear distance to the next stem or rib.

4. Wall panels in which the T-form is used only for the purpose of providing additional compression area should have a flange thickness at juncture of stem and flange not less than one-half the width of the stem and a total effective flange width not more than four times the width of the stem.

5. The overhanging portion of the flange of the ribbed or T-shaped wall panel should not be considered as effective in computing shear and diagonal tension resistance of the panel.

Hollow cored panels—

1. Panels made by extruding or casting hollow cores within the thickness of the panel should have the effective section computed taking into account the hollow cores.

2. Where panels are subjected to loads requiring transfer of shear between two faces of the panel, the thickness of connecting diaphrams should be designed for shear transfer through the concrete section.

3. Minimum thickness of the faces of the panel should be 3/4 in. except where fire rating or minimum reinforcement protection is not the governing factor.

4. Where hollow cores are elliptical or oblong, the minimum thickness of the concrete layer between connecting ribs should be determined by the requirements of maximum slenderness ratio required by stress.

Sandwich panels—

1. Sandwich panels consisting of two layers of concrete separated by a non-structural insulation core should have the two concrete layers positively connected together by monolithically cast concrete ribs or by positive mechanical shear ties. Shearing stress should not be transferred through the non-structural insulation core between the concrete layers. Compressive stress and bending stress should be carried by the concrete sections only.

2. Where the insulation core is a cellular or mineral aggregate lightweight concrete, shear stress transfer through the insulation core should not exceed the shear stress allowable through the weaker concrete.

3. Sandwich panels subjected to compressive stress should have the concrete layers tied together by ribs or mechanical ties at intervals in order that the h/t_e or l/t_e ratio of either concrete layer between the connecting ties does not exceed the governing h/t_e or l/t_e ratio of the total effective section of the sandwich panel.

Limiting dimensions—span, depth, and thickness

Precast wall panel used as non-bearing or curtain walls should be limited to a h/t (height or span to total thickness) ratio of 50, provided that the walls are designed to carry all loads which may be imposed on the unit and further provided that the deflection normal to the plane of the panel under loads is less than $h/240$, but not greater than 3/4 in., where h is the distance between supporting or enclosing members.

Where ceilings, floors and partitions intersect precast wall panels, the deflection normal to the plane of the panel as well as in its own plane should be limited to $h/360$ or 1/4 in. maximum, or provision made for panel movement and deflection in jointing details.

Precast wall panels spanning between columns, isolated foundations or other supporting members with depth/span ratios greater than 2/5 for continuous spans, or 4/5 for simple spans, should be designed as deep beams, taking into account the non-linear stress distribution, local buckling (especially in sandwich-type panels) and other pertinent effects.

The clear distances between lateral supports of a precast wall panel should not exceed 32 times the least width of the compression flange or effective panel thickness.

Precast wall panel anchors, connections, and lifting inserts

Wall panel units should be safely and adequately fastened in position by positive, mechanical connections and anchors capable of sustaining all loads and stresses due to shear bending or torsion which may be applied to the wall panel, including positive and negative wind pressures and earthquake forces where required by code.

All connections, anchors and inserts used to fasten panels to supporting frame should be made of materials sufficiently ductile to allow for limited panel movement due to shrinkage, moisture and temperature changes after panel erection to insure visible deformation before fracture.

Connectors, anchors and inserts should be designed for eccentric loading and combined shear bending and tension stresses to compensate for misalignment of panel connections to building frame of panel erection in the field.

Where welding is used for panel connections, welding should be performed in accordance with the recommended practice of the American Welding Society. All precautions should be taken during welding to minimize the effects of welding heat on the precast concrete wall panel or supporting concrete frame. All weld plates should be at least one-half inch thick and have a surface area at least twice the area of the connector being attached.

Where panel connections are exposed to corrosive action, the anchors, inserts and connectors should be made from corrosive resistant metals and materials.

Inserts used for lifting devices of precast concrete panels for fabrication and erection should be designed for 100 percent impact.

Panel connections should be fireproofed as required by local codes or to minimum fire resistance rating equivalent to that of the precast wall panel.

MANUFACTURING PROCESSES

Describes the manufacturing processes of precast concrete wall panels with various architectural treatments. Discusses texture, color, fabrication, consolidation, and aggregate exposure.

Precast Concrete Wall Panels: Manufacturing Processes

By Phillip W. Gutmann

■THE USE OF PRECAST PANELS as a facing material began early in the 20th century. The earliest article found on this subject was "Artistic and Commercially Practical Surface Finishes for Concrete Work," in the Apr. 3, 1909, issue of *Engineering Record.* However, the concept of precasting architectural concrete elements which constitute an entire wall system is comparatively new. These units fit into the types of construction that we know as curtain wall, or non-load-bearing elements, and load-bearing elements which could be columns, spandrel beams, or window boxes. Concrete wall panels may be divided into three major classes: panels precast complete with back-up; thin facing panels later backed up with block and mortar or other materials; and concrete sandwich panels consisting of two thin concrete panels enclosing a layer of insulating material.

PANEL TEXTURE AND COLOR

The variety and appearance of precast architectural concrete is almost unlimited since surfaces may range from rough, rugged textures to a glasslike smoothness. Almost any color combination can be achieved. Practically any shape, size, and curvature of panels can be obtained under various precast forming operations.

A common means of obtaining surface texture and color is exposing selected aggregates such as quartz, granites, colorful gravels, and certain marbles, plus various ceramic and vitreous materials. There is a wide range of colors and sizes available among these various aggregates which leaves the architect with a vast choice, depending upon the architectural concepts desired in a specific job. Surfaces manufactured in various plants can also be gray or white broomed concrete with a light to heavy texture. Also, a gray or white form finish can be obtained from striated plywood, plastic, rubber mats, muslin, and hand-rubbed surfaces. Tile facings, terra cotta, and metal-clad panels have been incorporated in many jobs adding to the wide range and versatility of this product.

There is, of course, no short cut that can be utilized in precasting work and still provide a highly durable and long-lasting product. The individual experience and skill of the workman and careful attention to the details in casting, curing, and finishing the panels constitute the essentials of good production.

FABRICATION

Generally the fabrication procedures for exposed aggregate precast concrete start with proper construction of the forms desired to produce a certain size and shape of panel. Steel, wood, concrete, and plastic, or any combination of these materials, can be used for complete form construction (Fig. 1). The requirements of different jobs vary and consequently the material or combination of materials for the forms will depend on many conditions such as: the number of reuses, tolerances, draft allowances, texture, vibration techniques, mass, production schedules, and locally available talent.

The surface of the mold which will be against the surface of the panel to be exposed is coated with a retardant (or bond breaker if other means of exposure are to be used such as acid dipping or sand blasting). A chemical retarder can be brushed or sprayed on the surface of the mold or a retarder-impregnated material can be fastened to those surfaces. One procedure often used is spreading the retarder on a muslin cloth which is then spread over the bottom of the forms. The muslin cloth can only be used when the shape of the form is applicable to maintaining a smooth surface of the cloth. The chemical retarder may be in a semi-dry or dry condition before the aggregates are placed in the form; and the concentration of the retarder can be varied to obtain the amount of aggregate reveal desired.

If extremely deep reveal is desired, in the range of more than 1/2 in., an absorbent bed such as sand is first sprinkled on the form to the required depth. The aggregates are then hand placed into this layer of sand (Fig. 3).

ACI member **Phillip W. Gutmann** is manager, Product Development, Medusa Portland Cement Company. He was formerly manager for operations, Marietta Concrete Division, Martin Marietta Corporation, and manager, Technical Division, Medusa Portland Cement Company.

Often it is found desirable to preplace aggregates and then spread sand throughout the voids. In this way an evenly exposed surface is more easily maintained.

After installation of the retarder or bond breaker and decorative aggregate, the cement matrix which will bind the aggregates is consolidated in the form. The cement matrix is generally a combination of white or grey portland cement, quartz, and silica sand or fine material recovered from the coarse aggregates. Extreme care must be taken to see that the concrete matrix flows evenly into all intricacies between the aggregate particles without disturbing their positions. Often the aggregates to be exposed are mixed with the matrix rather than hand placed, with care taken to assure their uniform distribution.

Adequate storage should be provided for aggregates to maintain a constant state of moisture and temperature in order to provide constant control of water requirements during mixing. The entire amount of aggregate needed in a particular job should be estimated and stockpiled before casting is started. In this way complete uniformity and brightness of aggregates can be obtained and the problem of variable aggregate from different areas of a quarry will be eliminated.

Reinforcement, if required to strengthen the panel, is placed on the back surface of the facing mix. This can vary from a wire mesh to light reinforcing bars, depending on the total thickness and size of the panel slab. The back-up concrete may contain lightweight aggregate. This will reduce the total weight of the slab thereby reducing stresses during the lifting, hauling, and erecting operations. The slump of the back-up concrete is generally low. The back-up concrete will contain metal fastening clips or inserts which are required to attach the panel to the structural frame of the building. The final casting operation is either internal or external vibration in order to achieve the necessary consolidation.

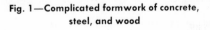

Fig. 1—Complicated formwork of concrete, steel, and wood

Fig. 2—Intricate negative wood formwork

Fig. 3—Hand placed surface aggregate

Fig. 4—Placement of mesh over insulation on precast exposed aggregate panel

CONSOLIDATION

Adequate and complete consolidation of the concrete is of primary importance in the manufacture of wall panels. Sufficient consolidation is achieved by a variety of methods in the precasting plants of the United States. However these methods of consolidation may be classified into: external vibration, internal vibration, and concrete consistency variation. Of course it is of utmost importance, regardless of the techniques, to obtain (1) pleasing appearance, (2) durability, and (3) economy. Most precasting plants obtain these desirable effects regardless of the consolidation process employed.

The process employing external vibration is usually achieved by installation of high frequency vibrators directly on the forms or through a vibrating table. These vibrators operate at frequencies generally in excess of 3600 vibrations per minute and with amplitudes less than 1/16 in. Vibrating tables or forms should have sufficient stiffness to apply the vibration uniformly over the surface of the panel. Recently, another method (shocked concrete) has been introduced into the United States—concrete with a low total water content placed in heavy wood forms on a low frequency table. The forms rise and fall approximately 3/8 in. at a rate of 260 times per minute. Through this process, concrete is thoroughly consolidated to provide a high strength and smooth finished concrete surface. These shocked panels are often textured with an acid etch or sand blast.

Internal vibration methods are accomplished by placing the architectural facing mixes to the required depth and then consolidating and compacting by means of a tamping type or "jitterbug" vibrator. Back-up mixes, generally of a lower consistency, are placed and vibrated in the same manner. At times a combination of high frequency external vibration and internal vibration is incorporated in this process.

A third procedure may be classified as consolidation by means of consistency. In this process, a rich high-slump, concrete is placed in the first layer to

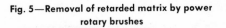

Fig. 5—Removal of retarded matrix by power rotary brushes

Fig. 6—Removal of matrix by acid washing

assure uniform distribution of the coarse aggregate and maximum consolidation. The mix of the following layers is progressively stiffer, thus allowing absorption of excessive water from the previous layer. Since uniform exposure of aggregate in deep sections of panels is often difficult to obtain, consolidation by variable consistency may offer a versatile method for obtaining such exposure. Excessive exposure of aggregate at maximum depths may be prevented by reduction of slump, and insufficient exposure at higher elevations may be overcome by the addition of coarse aggregate to the mix in upper sections. In this way, the necessary alterations of aggregate distribution, as affected by gravity forces, can be made. Regardless of the manufacturing process, the major quality aspects must be met: good consolidation, high strength, low absorption, pleasing appearance, and durability to freezing and thawing when exposed to the atmosphere.

FORM REMOVAL

When the panel has gained sufficient strength to resist the forces of form stripping and handling stresses, it is removed and set up against a framing system. Generally the strength of precast panels will permit stripping approximately 18 hr after casting. However, the exact time at which removal of the retarded matrix in a concrete facing is permissible is dependent on the type of panel face, the desired degree of exposure of the particles, the ambient temperature, the water-cement ratio, and curing techniques employed in the panel. The timing can only be determined by the experience of each individual plant, depending on their particular materials and methods.

AGGREGATE EXPOSURE

Exposure of aggregates can be obtained by hand brushing or the application of powered rotary brushes (Fig. 5) and sometimes belt sanding equipment. Acid washing is usually done 3 to 7 days after casting, depending on the

Fig. 7—Removal of matrix by acid washing

Fig. 8—Sand blasting for aggregate exposure

type of portland cement. The time of exposure during sand blasting will vary depending upon the etch required, aggregates employed, and the compressive strength of the concrete at various times of curing. Also, the gradation and hardness of the sand employed plus variations in sand-blasting equipment will alter the timing of exposure. All methods of exposure must be studied for a particular job prior to production. This must be done so that the effect of water-cement ratio, compaction, curing techniques, and mix proportions can be determined. The slab is then sprayed with water and further scrubbed to remove any loose particles of mortar from the surface. Following this operation a 12-hr steam curing or a 2- or 3-day wet curing process is initiated. Generally, the surface is again cleaned after the curing period, perhaps with a mild solution of muriatic acid. A sealer is sometimes applied over the entire surface.

Since the advent of more efficient air conditioning and heating, the problem of insulation has become an important factor for consideration in all parts of the United States. The commonly known sandwich panel is a type of construction that will provide good insulating properties. Here an insulation of fiber glass, foamed polystyrene or polyurethane, foamed glass, or foamed concrete may be inserted between the backup and facing mix. Sandwich panels are generally 4 to 8 in., thick, depending on insulation and structural requirements.

GENERAL PRODUCTION CONSIDERATIONS

Many problems normally regarded in the concrete industry as minor become of major importance in the production of precast architectural concrete. Variations in aggregate size, texture, and specific gravity must be considered in regard to bond strength, compressive strength, and consolidation. Also the influence of various cement chemistries and water requirements on early strengths, consistency, and reaction with retarders must be considered. Before a specific job is ready to begin production, an entire review of the material performance must be weighed against the architectural desires of the job Concrete quality must be balanced with architectural requirements.

All necessary decisions on type of forms, concrete consistency, and means of exposure must actually be done by plant experimentation and testing before final manufacturing decisions can be made. Only correctly employed techniques will provide the most economical method of production plus providing a pleasing appearance and durable product for the final consumer.

BOWING, WARPAGE, AND MOVEMENT

Investigations were made on several existing buildings, and the results analyzed. Some tentative conclusions as to bowing, warpage, and movement are presented here fur further discussion and study.

Precast Concrete Wall Panels:

Bowing, Warpage, and

Movement

By Sheng Pao Sheng

■THE USE OF PRECAST CONCRETE WALL PANELS has made it possible to build the substructure and superstructure of a building at the same time. While concrete footings are being placed in the field, walls are cast in the plant. The construction time can be reduced considerably. An average sized panel unit (say 8 x 8 ft) could easily be a wall of a room complete with exterior and interior finish. The advantage of this new construction method has attracted the attention of building industry, but the large unit with concrete as basic material has its limitations due to the physical properties of concrete. These limitations must be studied and analyzed before the panels can be properly designed and applied.

The concept of precast concrete wall panels is partly developed from the idea of "cast stone" which is used as facing material, especially for exterior walls. Normally the size of cast stone is approximately 4 x 4 ft. In the early period of panel development the maximum dimensions were seldom over 10 ft. In the process of evolution it was learned that precast concrete panels can be used not only as facing material, but also as self-supporting structural wall units, spanning from column to column or floor to floor. Large erection equipment and convenience of transportation have also contributed to the growing trend. The size of panels, in the past 10 years, has increased up to

30 ft or more. Now, a panel 40, 50, or even 60 ft in length or height is well in sight.

While panel users are enjoying the advantage of large panels they are also encountering difficulties. Perhaps the most intangible problems are those involving bowing, warpage and movement of panels.

CAUSES OF BOWING, WARPAGE, AND MOVEMENT

Bowing is usually referred to as the deflection of a flexural member in a single plane. Warpage is bowing out a single plane or two-way bowing. Since the amount of "out of plane" is usually small the problem could, therefore, be narrowed down to one way bowing. Movement is the change of bowing or warpage relative to a time factor.

The causes of bowing, warpage, and movement of a concrete member are directly related to the physical properties of concrete. Concrete expands, contracts, and creeps due to variations in temperature and moisture, chemical reaction of hardening, and external forces.

To study the effect of temperature differential let us suggest the following hypothetical problem for the purpose of illustration as shown in Fig. 1.

Neglecting the time lag and other factors in the process of heating or cooling the difference in length between the exterior and interior surface, may be assumed as,

$$\epsilon = 0.0000065 \times 100 \times 24 \times 12 = 0.19 \text{ in.}$$

To calculate the amount of deflection (see Fig. 2).

$$\tan \theta = \frac{0.19}{2 \times 5} \approx 0.019$$

$$\theta = 1°5' \qquad 2\theta = 2°10'$$

Radius of curvature:

$$\rho = \frac{360 \times 24 \times 12}{2\pi \times 2.2} = 7500 \text{ in.}$$

Deflection due to the temperature differential:

$$\Delta_T = \rho \left(1 - \cos\theta\right) = 7500 \left(1 - 0.99982\right) = 1.35 \text{ in.}$$

Now, using the same example and assuming the difference of relative humidity of 50 percent between the two faces of the panel, apply Schorer's[1] formula of shrinkage coefficient:

$$\delta_f = \frac{0.125 \, (0.90 - h)}{100} = \frac{0.125 \, (0.90 - 0.50)}{100} = 0.0005 \text{ in. per in.}$$

ACI member **Sheng Pao Sheng,** consulting engineer, Williamstown, W. Va., was chief engineer, Marietta Concrete Division, Martin Marietta Corporation, before entering private practice.

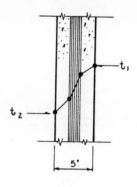

Fig. 1—Temperature differential

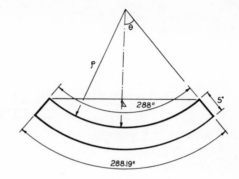

Fig. 2—Notation and demensions

where δ_f is the volumetric change of concrete and h is the differential relative humidity of concrete in decimals. For a panel of 24 ft span:

$$\Sigma\delta_f = 0.0005 \times 288 = 0.144 \text{ in.}$$

$$\tan\theta = \frac{0.144}{2 \times 5} = 0.0144$$

$$\theta = 0°50' \qquad 2\theta = 1°40'$$

Radius of curvature:

$$\rho = \frac{360 \times 24 \times 12}{2\pi \times 1.67} = 9900 \text{ in.}$$

Deflection due to relative humidity differential:

$$\Delta_M = \rho (1-\cos\theta) = 9900 (1 - 0.99989) = 1.09 \text{ in.}$$

Thirdly, to study the effect of external force let us assume the wind load simulates a uniformly distributed load of 30 lb per sq ft. The deflection due to wind load will be:

$$\Delta_W = \frac{5wL^4}{384EI} = 0.46 \text{ in.}$$

where the moment of inertia $I = 122$ in.^{4} and the modulus of elasticity $E = 4 \times 10^6$ psi.

Fourthly, suppose that the panel were cured in the yard by leaning against an A-frame. Deflection due to creep will occur especially along the upper edge (Fig. 3). Let us apply Shank's[2] creep formula.

$$\delta_t = c\sqrt[r]{t} = 0.30 \times 10^{-6} \text{ (estimated typical value)}$$

where δ_t = specific creep in millionths, c = coefficient of creep strain, r = root deduced from tests, and t = time of duration of loading in days (30).

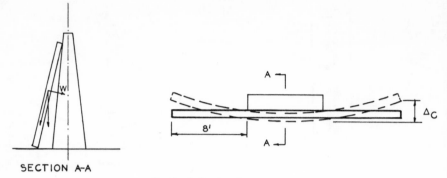

SECTION A-A

Fig. 3—Deflection due to creep

Assume the modulus of elasticity $E = 4 \times 10^6$ psi.

$$\text{Axial elastic strain} = \frac{1}{4 \times 10^6} = 0.25 \times 10^{-6} \text{ per psi}$$

$$\text{Total strain} = (0.30 + 0.25) \times 10^{-6} = 0.55 \times 10^{-6} \text{ per psi}$$

$$\text{Sustained modulus } E_{ct} = \frac{1}{0.55 \times 10^6} = 1.8 \times 10^6 \text{ psi}$$

If $w = 12$ lb per sq ft (Fig. 3), the deflection of 8 ft cantilever will be

$$\Delta_c = \frac{wL^4}{8E_{ct}I} = 0.05 \text{ in.}$$

DISCUSSION

If all those factors given above were additive—as one might suspect—the total bowing (including certain amount of movement) of the panel would be:

$$\Sigma\Delta = 1.35 + 1.09 + 0.46 + 0.05 = 2.95 \text{ in.}$$

Investigation shows, however, that, on the average, bowing and movement of this size panel is only about 3/4 in. The following might be suggested as possible explanations.

Firstly, it is quite obvious that the factors are not additive, because temperature differential will produce an effect that is ultimately opposite to that of moisture differential. That is to say, if the sun shines on the exterior surface of a panel or a heat stream comes in contact with the inside surface of a panel, the surface temperature will eventually rise. The concrete will consequently lose moisture and eventually decrease the relative humidity in the concrete. As a result, these two factors cancel each other to a certain extent. The total bowing will become:

$$\Sigma\Delta = 1.35 - 1.09 + 0.46 + 0.05 = 0.77 \text{ in.}$$

Secondly, according to Washa's[3] shrinkage test data, 75 percent of the drying shrinkage will take place in 90 days. The temperature and shrinkage reinforcing steel in resisting shortening of concrete puts the concrete in tension.

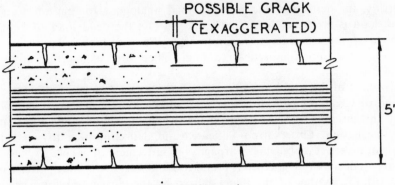

Fig. 4—Surface cracks

The shortened dimension will likely be distributed in the form of minute cracks or absorbed as a factor of porosity in the concrete (Fig. 4).

The cracks, though small, will serve as an "absorber." The movement or change of bowing experienced at an earlier stage, will be absorbed by opening or closing of the cracks. The residual movement therefore will be only 25 percent of the amount after 90 days of curing. The problem will then be reduced to merely bowing. Investigation indicated that movement of the panel will be greatly reduced or practically undetectable after a certain length of time or as soon as any visible cracks appear on the panel.

Thirdly, in examining the actual construction of a sandwich panel (Fig. 5), we may visualize that the member resembles a Vierendeel truss. The upper and lower chord of the truss are not rigidly connected. That leaves the two outer edges to resist the relative sliding movement between the inside and outside slabs. The flexibility and deformation of the edges caused by the sliding force should eliminate part of the deflection due to span length differential of the two faces of the panel.

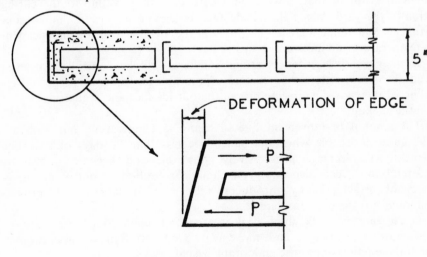

Fig. 5—Section of sandwich panel

Fourthly, the deflection due to wind load analogous to that of sustained uniform load is far from the actual value. In fact the dead load of concrete must be taken into consideration. Quite often the dead load is larger in magnitude than the superimposed wind load. Therefore, its inertia cannot be neglected.

This phase of the problem can be compared with a typical example of conservation of linear momentum. Nearly all of the kinetic energy is dissipated as heat and internal work or used up for producing sound and vibration or minute oscillation. Observation indicated the deflection due to wind load has little or no effect on bowing, warpage, and movement of panels.

Fifthly, deflection due to creep is found to be almost a constant. After curing in the yard, the camber of the panel caused by the curing condition becomes a permanent set. Even though there will be a slight recovery after the panel is erected in vertical position, the minute tensile cracks cannot be completely closed. The span length of the exterior face will be always longer than the inside face. This is an independent factor that can determine the amount of bowing and warpage.

CONCLUSION AND SUMMARY

1. Precast concrete wall panels with concrete as basic material will bow, warp, and move. Its magnitude can be predicted and controlled but not completely eliminated.

2. Investigation indicates that panels always deflect outward regardless of whether the temperature is higher or lower inside than outside, whether the panel is solid or sandwiched, or whether the panel is cast face down for the exposed aggregate panels or cast face up for the regular concrete broomed surface.

Initial curing before lifting out of form is not a significant factor of the problem. It is found that bowing and warpage is largely due to the curing position in the yard. When the inside face is leaning against a slanted support the bending moment creates a camber in the member which is independent from temperature and moisture change.

3. By maneuvering curing positions camber could be controlled or even utilized to compensate other factors—for instance, the shrinkage differential between exposed aggregate mix in the outside face and regular aggregate mix in the backup.

4. The amount of movement due to changing temperature and moisture can be quite noticeable when the panels are less than 90 days of age. The movement will decrease progressively, however, and become unmeasurable after 1 to 3 years depending on climatic conditions. Control of movement could be achieved by introducing false joints in large panels providing handling stresses are considered.

5. Great care must be applied if intermediate connections are used to control bowing, warpage, and movement. Concentration of stresses may occur at these points and cause undesirable visual cracks.

REFERENCES

1. Schorer, H., "Prestressed Concrete Design Principles and Reinforced Units," ACI Journal, *Proceedings* V. 39, No. 4, June 1963, pp. 493–528.

2. Shank, J. R., "The Plastic Flow of Concrete," *Bulletin,* No. 91, Ohio State University Engineering Experiment Station, Sept. 1935.

3. Washa, G. W., "Basic Reinforced Concrete Design," by G. E. Large, p. 328.

SANDWICH PANELS

Describes an investigation of the structural behavior of 31 concrete sandwich panels tested under uniform flexural loading. Panel designs included different types of insulating core materials and different methods of providing positive shear connections between the reinforced concrete shells.

Precast Concrete Wall Panels: Flexural Stiffness of Sandwich Panels

By D. W. Pfeifer and J. A. Hanson

■CONCRETE SANDWICH PANELS have become an important feature in modern building construction as they offer, in a single building element, an economical method of providing structural requirements, thermal insulation, and attractive architectural treatment. Extremely light weight insulating materials such as foamed concrete, plastics, and glass provide good insulation, but they have low resistance to handling and service loads. A protective or load-bearing structural concrete shell must be provided over one or both sides of these materials. These shells also provide a convenient means of imparting architectural treatment to the wall. Attractive surfaces may be obtained by many methods, such as exposed aggregate or patterns obtained from three-dimensional forms. The purpose of this report is to contribute to a better understanding of the structural design of sandwich panels, rather than to discuss either insulation or architecture.

The face shells of sandwich panels must not only provide protection to the insulation and meet the immediate demands of handling and imposed loads, but must continue to give satisfactory performance under long-time service. Exposure conditions cause temperature and moisture differentials in sandwich construction and these conditions may have a more pronounced effect on the satisfactory long-time structural behavior than do the imposed loads.[1,2,3]

Sandwich panels used in North America generally have 1 to 2 in. of insulation sandwiched between two identically sized shells 1-1/2 to 2-1/2 in. thick. The European counterpart, however, usually consists of a 4-in. load-bearing interior shell with 1 in. of insulation and a 2 in. outer concrete shell. Load-bearing construction is generally used in Europe while curtain wall construction is more common here.

TESTING PROGRAM AND PROCEDURE

It was the purpose of this laboratory study to investigate the effects of certain design features, such as type of insulation, thickness of panel, or inclusion of positive shear-resisting connections between the shells, on the capacity of sandwich panels to perform satisfactorily their function of space enclosure. For this purpose some 50 panels were fabricated and tested in the laboratory. Of these, 31 have been chosen to illustrate the more important structural implications of the laboratory study.

A specimen size of 3 x 5 ft was chosen as adequate for the study and convenient for testing a large number of panels. This size, although smaller than most panels in service, was of sufficient span to obtain uniform bending in the flexure test and also to allow the use of at least three continuous shear connectors (either metal or concrete ribs) in the longer dimension. Some panels without metal or concrete shear connectors were also included. Overall thickness of the laboratory specimens varied from 2-1/4 to 6 in., although the 5-in. panel with 2 in. of insulation was employed for the greater number of tests. The panels varied in weight from 10 to 35 lb per sq ft of wall area, depending on the thickness of the panel and type of insulation. The program included five types of insulating cores, three types of metal shear connectors, and various configurations of plain concrete as shear connectors between the structural concrete shells. Duplicate specimens were not generally tested, but evidence of reproducible results was furnished by the similar behavior of panels containing different types of plastic insulation.

All panels reported in this study were tested to flexural failure. The flexural test was chosen to study the structural behavior of the sandwich panels, not because lateral loading is generally critical in this type of construction, but because deflection measurement under uniform loading offered a sensitive and precise procedure for assessing the relative stiffness characteristics of the different panel construction systems. The resistance to warping under differential temperature and moisture conditions or under loading may then be achieved by incorporating the required stiffness into the panel design.

ACI member **Donald W. Pfeifer**, development engineer, Products and Applications Development Section, Portland Cement Association, Research and Development Laboratories, Skokie, Ill., is a member of ACI Committee 223, Expansive Cement Concretes.

ACI member **J. A. Hanson**, manager, Products and Applications Development Section, Portland Cement Association Research and Development Laboratories, Skokie, Ill., is chairman of ACI Committee 213, Lightweight Aggregates and Lightweight Aggregate Concrete, and a member of 533, Precast Panels, and 435, Deflection of Concrete Building Structures.

Materials

Aggregate and concrete mix—The lightweight aggregate used in the concrete shells was an expanded shale produced in a rotary kiln with the raw material pre-sized prior to burning. The particles are generally rounded and sealed. A typical screen analysis and the dry loose unit weights for the commercial medium and fine size fractions are given in Table 1.

In accordance with the method of "Recommended Practice for Selecting Proportions for Structural Lightweight Concrete (ACI 613A-59)," the air-dry lightweight aggregates were mixed with two-thirds of the required water for 2 min. The remaining water, the air-entraining agent, and the cement were then added, and mixing continued for 3 min. A blend of four commercial brands of Type I cements was used. The mix proportions are given in Table 2.

Shell reinforcing steel—The structural concrete shells of the sandwich panels were reinforced with welded wire fabric conforming to ASTM A82-62T, "Cold-Drawn Steel Wire for Concrete Reinforcement." The steel wire in this reinforcement has an ultimate strength of approximately 70,000 psi. Shell reinforcement was not considered a variable in this study and the shells of most panels contained a single layer of 2 x 2-14/14 welded wire fabric. However, two panels were reinforced with 6 x 6-8/8 fabric. This variation in steel area provided some insight into the effect of reinforcement style on panel deflection, but the range of the chosen steel areas was not sufficient to indicate the effect of the amount of reinforcement on cracking moment resistance.

Metal shear connectors—The majority of the sandwich panels contained metal shear connectors between the concrete shells. Three types of connectors were used: (1) expanded metal (3/4 in. No. 16-18, flattened), shaped into a channel section and then tied to the shell reinforcement (Fig. 1); (2) a commercial truss member (top and bottom chords of double 7-gage wires and web

TABLE 1—AGGREGATE GRADATION

Sieve size	Cumulative percent retained, by weight	
	Medium	Fine
3/8 in.	0	0
No. 4	57.8	0
No. 8	96.9	24.6
No. 16	100.0	54.4
No. 30	100.0	73.7
No. 50	100.0	86.0
No. 100	100.0	93.0
	100.0	100.0
Fineness modulus	5.55	3.32
Dry loose unit weight, lb per cu ft	47.2	58.0

TABLE 2—MIX PROPORTIONS

Cement . . . . 6.94 bags (652 lb)*

Water . . . . 381 lb*

Total aggregate (air dried) . . . . . . 1576 lb*

Fine (50.7 percent by volume) . . . 879 lb*

Medium (49.3 percent by volume) . 697 lb*

Air (Rollo-Meter) . . . . 6.1 percent

Plastic unit weight . . . . 96.8 pcf

Slump . . . . 2-3/4 in.

*Per cu yd of concrete.

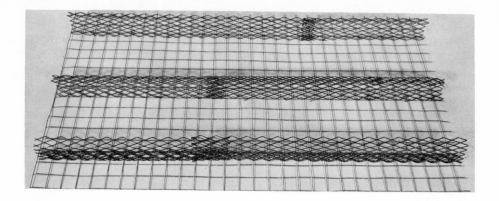

Fig. 1—Channel-shaped expanded metal shear connectors tied to welded wire shell reinforcement

members of single 7-gage wire) which required only tying to the shell reinforcement (Fig. 2); and (3) welded wire fabric (2 x 2-14/14) folded up from the lower shell and tied at the bends at the bottom of the fold to form a shear connector of a double vertical layer of the wire fabric.

Insulation—The insulating materials were commercially available rigid board stock or batting: one foamed polyurethane plastic, two foamed polystyrene plastics, one glass fiber, one foamed glass, and one autoclaved cellular concrete. The mechanical properties of these core materials, as obtained from the manufacturers, are given in Table 3.

Fabrication and curing of specimens

The sandwich panels were cast in a form mounted on a high-frequency vibrating table. The bottom shell reinforcement and shear connectors were tied together and then positioned in the form (Fig. 3). A predetermined weight of lightweight concrete, sufficient to provide the proper shell thickness, was vibrated into place, and the insulation was then placed between the shear

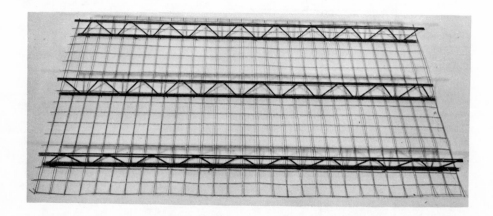

Fig. 2—Commercial trussed shear connectors tied to welded wire shell reinforcement

TABLE 3—MECHANICAL PROPERTIES OF INSULATING CORES*

Properties	Foamed polyurethane	Foamed polystyrene	Glass fiber	Foamed glass	Autoclaved cellular concrete
Unit weight, pcf	1.6–2.0	1.6–2.0	6.0	9.0	23.0
Mod. of Elasticity, psi	. . . . . .	1000	. . . . . .	180,000	173,000
Shear strength, psi	. . . . . .	27–36	. . . . . .	40	. . . . . .
Flexural strength, psi	30–60	42–61	. . . . . .	75	50
Compressive strength, psi	15	16–32	. . . . . .	100	400
Thermal conductivity at 70 F, Btu/hr/sq ft/F/in.	0.15	0.28	0.24	0.39	0.48

*Data from manufacturers.

connectors (Fig. 4). The reinforcement for the top shell was tied to the shear connector (Fig. 5) and the concrete for the top shell was cast and vibrated into place. The panels were moist-cured under polyethylene film for seven days at 73F and then allowed to dry at 73F and 50 percent relative humidity for 21 days. Compressive strength and tensile splitting strength determinations were made on 6 x 12-in. cylinders fabricated and cured under the same conditions. The sandwich panels and cylinders were tested at age 28 days.

Testing

The panels were tested in flexure under uniform loading, using an inflated plastic bag in combination with a 1,000,000-lb. hydraulic compression machine (Fig. 6). The 3 x 5-foot panel was positioned on the air-filled plastic bag contained within the stiffened wooden frame located on the testing machine base. The air pressure in the bag was then reduced until the panel was level and the bottom concrete shell was in complete contact with the air bag. The testing machine head was lowered until the reaction beams were in contact with the panel. A spherical head was placed between the rigid testing machine head and the load-distributing beam, and the effects of horizontal thrust were eliminated by roller bearings placed between the distributing beam and the reaction beams.

Variable loading was applied to the panel by increasing the air pressure in the plastic bag. Air pressure was regulated by a sensitive, flow-type regulator attached to the utility air supply. The total reaction of the air pressure on the panel was recorded from the low-range dials of the static testing machine. Transverse deflection was indicated by three dial gages located at midspan, the average of which was in turn referred to the average of dial gages located at each of the four corners. Relative horizontal shear movement between the shells was measured by dial gages mounted at each end of the panel as indicated at the extreme right of Fig. 6.

Preliminary tests indicated that more reliable zero-load dial gage readings were obtained after pre-loading and unloading the panel. Consequently the panels were tested through two cycles, the first to somewhat less than estimated initial flexural cracking, and the second to ultimate failure. The loads

Fig. 3—Shear connectors and bottom shell reinforcement in position

Fig. 4—Insulation positioned between shear connectors after bottom concrete shell was cast

Fig. 5—Tying top shell reinforcement to the metal shear connectors

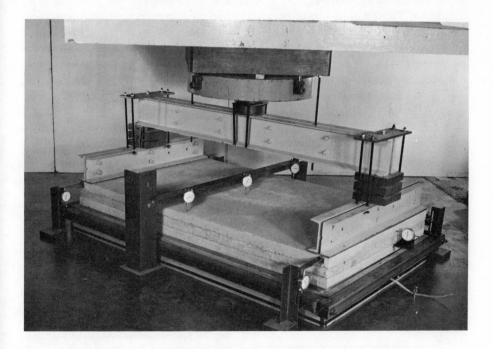

Fig. 6—Flexural test arrangement

were applied in increments of 500 lb (33 lb per sq ft) and each increment was maintained for a period sufficient to record the deflection readings and mark the flexural cracking progression. Complete testing for the two cycles required approximately 1 hr.

TEST RESULTS

Construction details and test results for the 31 sandwich wall panels are presented in Table 4, along with the physical properties of the companion 6 x 12-in. cylinders. The recorded values for cylinder properties are the average of two compression and four tensile splitting tests each. These data were obtained with specimens from approximately 30 sets of four concrete batches mixed over a period of several months. The accompanying coefficients of variation are quite typical for replicate laboratory mixes over this extended period. The effect of these variations in concrete properties on the analyses of the panel tests has been minimized by the particular failure criteria discussed below.

Table 4 presents bending moment capacities rather than magnitude of uniform loading to facilitate comparison with other panel designs. Fig. 7 shows the moment-deflection curves for five typical panels. A linear relationship during the early loading continues to the point of initial flexural cracking. A change in the slope of the deflection curve occurs at this point, or, as in the case of the panel without shear connectors, the moment-deflection relationship becomes curvilinear. The type of failure occurring in each panel is listed in Table 4. These failures have been classified as either tension or shear. Tension failure was defined as rupture of the shell reinforcement at maximum moment, while shear failure was established by large relative horizontal movements between the two shells. Fig. 8 is typical of the cracking pattern in the tested panels.

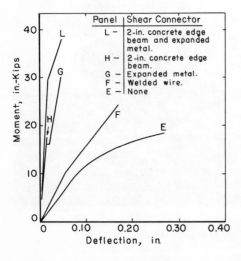

Fig. 7—Typical flexural behavior of 5-in. sandwich panels with 2-in. plastic insulation to 50 percent of ultimate strength

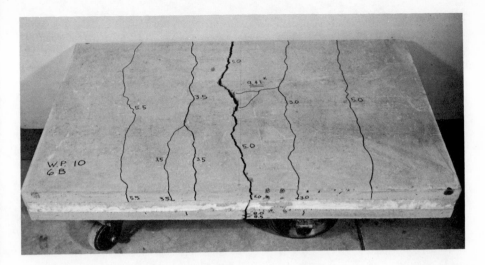

Fig. 8—Typical cracking pattern after flexural test

Concrete sandwich construction has been characterized by thin concrete shells and thin insulating cores. The use of minimum reinforcement cover and the possible loss of thermal effectiveness of certain types of insulation when moist, require wall panel designs that assure crack free performance. Although the test loads were carried to complete failure, the analyses of the effects of the test variables have thus been limited to loadings less than those which caused flexural cracking. Pertinent tests have been selected from Table 4 to illustrate the effects of these variables and are presented as moment-deflection curves to the point of flexural cracking. Each of these curves is labeled with the panel designation provided by the first column of the table.

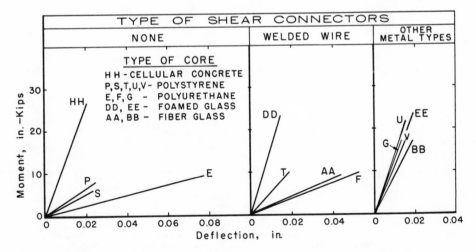

Fig. 9—Flexural behavior to initial cracking of 5-in. sandwich panels as affected by type of insulating core

Type of core insulation

The inclusion in the program of several types of lightweight insulating cores permitted comparison of the flexural behavior of the panels as affected by the type of insulating core. Fig. 9 presents the applied moment-deflection histories to initial flexural cracking of 5-in. panels with 2 in. of insulation and three types of shear connectors. Wide variation, depending on the type of

TABLE 4—SANDWICH PANEL

Details of sandwich panel construction

Panel	Insulation type	Panel thickness, in.	Insulation thickness, in.	Type of shear connector	Reinforcing[a] steel in.^{2}
A	Polyurethane	2-1/4	1	Truss member	0.238
B	Polyurethane	2-1/2	1	Expanded metal	0.090[c]
C	Polyurethane	2-1/2	1	135,1 in. dia. concrete posts	0.090
D	Polyurethane	4	2	Welded wire fabric	0.090
E	Polyurethane	6	2	None	0.090
F	Polyurethane	5	2	Welded wire fabric	0.090
G	Polyurethane	5	2	Expanded metal	0.090[c]
H	Polyurethane	5	2	2 in. concrete edge rib	0.090
J	Polyurethane	5	2	22,2-1/2 in. dia. concrete posts	0.090
K	Polyurethane	5	2	1-1/2 in. concrete end rib	0.090
L	Polyurethane	5	2	2 in. concrete edge rib and expanded metal	0.090[c]
M	Polyurethane	6	2	Welded wire fabric	0.090
N	Polystyrene	3-1/2	1-1/2	Truss member	0.238
P	Polystyrene	5	2	None	0.090
R	Polystyrene	5	2	None	0.123[b]
S	Polystyrene	5	2	None	0.090
T	Polystyrene	5	2	Welded wire fabric	0.090
U	Polystyrene	5	2	Truss member	0.238
V	Polystyrene	5	2	Truss member	0.238
W	Polystyrene	5	2	Expanded metal	0.123[b,c]
X	Polystyrene	5	2	135,1 in. dia. concrete posts	0.090
Y	Polystyrene	5	2	1-1/2 in. concrete edge rib	0.090
Z	Polystyrene	6	2	Truss member	0.238
AA	Glass fiber	5	2	Welded wire fabric	0.090
BB	Glass fiber	5	2	Truss member	0.238
CC	Glass fiber	5	2	Truss member	0.238
DD	Foamed glass	5	2	Welded wire fabric	0.090
EE	Foamed glass	5	2	Truss member	0.238
FF	Autoclaved	3	1-1/2	None	0.090
GG	Cellular	3-1/2	1-1/2	None	0.090
HH	Concrete	5	2	None	0.090

[a] Longitudinal steel area per single shell.
[b] 6 × 6—8/8 welded wire fabric shell reinforcement.
[c] Contribution of flanges of expanded metal shear connectors not included.
[d] Relative end movement of concrete shells.
[e] End movement not measured.
[f] Failure by crushing under reaction.

core, may be noted in the case of panels without shear connectors and of those with welded wire shear connectors. When more efficient types of metal shear connectors are provided (right side of Fig. 9), the effect of the core type is much less pronounced and the variation in flexural stiffness is greatly reduced, at least for panels containing the plastic or glass insulations.

Consideration of the three diagrams of Fig. 9 indicates that the moment

DETAILS AND TEST RESULTS

Flexural test results					6 x 12-in. Cylinder test results		
Cracking moment, in.-kips	Deflection at cracking, in.	Horiz. shear[d] displacement at cracking, in.	Ultimate moment, in.-kips	Type of failure	Compressive strength, psi	Modulus of elasticity, psi	Tensile splitting strength, psi
8.72	0.095	0.002	38.50	Shear	5770	2.36×10^b	279
12.54	0.102	[e]	21.75	Tension	5680	2.33	364
8.72	0.099	[e]	11.17	Shear	5760	2.47	309
9.11	0.087	0.014	31.54	Shear	5710	2.25	286
9.11	0.075	0.011	37.34	Tension	4930	2.21	284
9.80	0.052	0.006	48.71	Tension	5200	2.25	288
16.36	0.012	0.002	60.06	Tension	6000	2.41	302
16.36	0.011	0.000	36.46	Tension	6330	2.40	303
9.80	0.056	0.003	34.00	Tension	5700	2.39	296
15.65	0.050	0.002	22.24	Tension	5980	2.38	317
29.40	0.017	[e]	75.17	Tension	6320	2.51	293
19.60	0.025	0.002	61.54	Tension	5350	2.22	275
16.27	0.041	0.002	68.01	Tension	5660	2.30	272
8.13	0.025	0.003	31.34	Shear	5670	2.23	306
9.80	0.048	0.003	28.32	Shear	5780	2.42	322
6.17	0.023	0.004	36.46	Tension	5860	2.37	289
9.80	0.018	0.002	43.61	Tension	6680	2.48	271
21.56	0.015	0.001	84.86	Tension	6260	2.39	283
16.36	0.014	0.001	83.60	Tension	6100	2.37	306
19.60	0.033	0.001	76.44	Tension	5720	2.43	310
18.91	0.015	0.001	29.39	Tension	5000	2.17	269
19.60	0.012	0.000	39.00	Tension	5860	2.30	267
24.50	0.011	0.000	104.86	Tension	5330	2.25	292
9.11	0.043	0.005	22.25	Shear	5140	2.17	284
16.27	0.018	0.001	58.80	[f]	6270	2.39	294
16.27	0.012	0.000	59.75	[f]	5810	2.27	307
22.83	0.014	0.000	37.84	Tension	5980	2.31	288
22.83	0.019	0.000	75.77	Tension	6130	2.32	274
5.78	0.027	[e]	16.76	Tension	5670	2.42	354
9.11	0.020	[e]	20.67	Tension	5880	2.41	279
26.16	0.020	0.000	40.48	Tension	6260	2.43	328
			Average		5800	2.34	296
			Coefficient of variation, percent		6.8	5.8	9.5

capacity of panels containing plastic or fiber glass core materials is relatively low, with some improvement gained with the use of the truss-type or expanded metal shear connectors. On the other hand, the plastic materials provide the highest thermal insulation values and are quite moisture resistant. Fiber glass is also a good insulator in the dry state but is capable of absorbing large quantities of moisture from the concrete or through transmission, thus losing a considerable amount of insulation value.

Panels with cellular concrete or foamed glass cores showed a relatively high value of moment resistance. It might be assumed that this improved behavior is the result of better bond of the core material to the concrete shells with consequent higher resistance to horizontal shearing forces. However, an examination of the relative horizontal shearing displacements between the concrete shells (Table 4), to the point of initial cracking, shows only negligible differences between the various panel designs. The superior flexural resistance and low deflection of the cellular concrete and foam glass panels may then be ascribed to the effect of their higher modulus of elasticity (Table 3). Reported values for these two materials are in the neighborhood of 175,000 psi, while the modulus of elasticity of the plastic foams is approximately 1000 psi.

Panel HH (cellular concrete insulation), fabricated without shear connectors, exhibited superior flexural performance even when compared with metal shear-connected panels containing other core materials. Some precautions should be observed in the use of this type of material as certain products with high absorption may cause excessive dessication of the freshly cast concrete shells. The use of the cellular concrete core in the oven-dry state, as provided by the autoclave, is highly desirable from the standpoint of a high insulation value. Maintenance of this dry state may be obtained with the application of a semi-waterproof coating which does not hamper adequate bond of the shells to the insulation material. A spray coat of a silicone mixture, as used in this investigation, may provide the necessary requirements of waterproofing and bond.

The relatively high flexural cracking resistance of Panel DD (foamed glass insulation with welded wire shear connectors) may be somewhat surprising in view of previous experience with this type of composite construction. Small

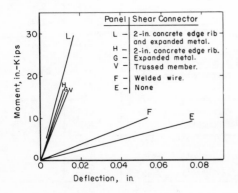

Fig. 10—Flexural behavior to initial cracking as affected by various types of shear connectors in 5-in. sandwich panels with 2-in. plastic insulation

samples of a single layer of concrete cast on a slab of foamed glass have generally indicated a high degree of bond between the layers, but after a relatively
short time of drying at normal temperatures and humidities, a separation
may occur within the foamed glass, probably due to the combination of normal drying shrinkage in the concrete and low shearing resistance of the glass.

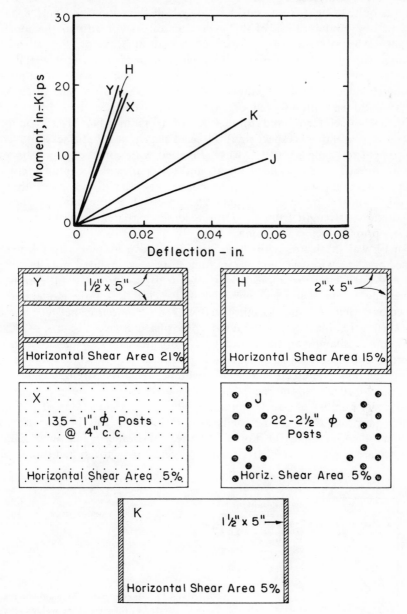

Fig. 11—Flexural behavior to initial cracking as affected by the amount and distribution of the
concrete shear connectors in 5-in. sandwich panels with 2-in. plastic insulation

Panel DD was fabricated with welded wire shear connectors between the shells. Although, as considered in the following discussion, this type of metal shear connection is relatively inefficient, it may have been sufficient to prevent a separation plane in the foamed glass insulation of the panel.

Type of shear connector

It was quite evident from consideration of all the sandwich panel tests that the type and configuration of the shear connectors constituted the most important test variables affecting improved structural behavior. Fig. 10 presents a comparison of the typical effects of six different shear connector installations, ranging from Panel E with no shear connector to Panel L with a combination of concrete edge ribs and expanded metal shear connectors. The three panels which contained unreinforced concrete edge ribs, three lines of expanded metal in channel form, and three lines of truss member shear connectors (Panels H, G, and V, respectively), indicate nearly equal stiffness and cracking moment resistance. Panel L was fabricated with concrete edge ribs which were reinforced with expanded metal, and this panel also contained two interior lines of expanded metal shear connectors. It will be noted that this additional shear connection had only a small effect on the panel stiffness but the additional strength from the reinforced ribs apparently doubled the load capacity prior to flexural cracking.

Panel F was fabricated with three interior lines of welded wire fabric shear connectors. The wires in these shear connectors were oriented only in the vertical and horizontal directions and consequently contributed little resistance to shearing action. The shear behavior of Panel F was only moderately improved over that of Panel E, fabricated with no connection between the concrete shells other than that contributed by the plastic foam.

It is quite common in the industry to fabricate sandwich panels with solid concrete edge ribs. Such ribs contribute greatly to the protection of the panel during handling and erection as well as adding structural strength. Due to the bulk of these edge ribs, the reduction of insulated area is sometimes considered excessive. A number of panels containing various configurations of plain concrete connections between the shells were included in this investigation with the aim of maintaining the horizontal shear resistance while increasing the insulated area. Plan views of five plane concrete connector systems and a com-

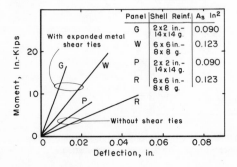

Fig. 12—Flexural behavior to initial cracking as affected by the style of the welded wire shell reinforcement in 5-in. sandwich panels with 2-in. plastic insulation

parison of the measured flexural resistance of each are shown in Fig. 11. The concrete area available for horizontal shear resistance, expressed as a percentage of the total horizontal area of the panel, is shown on each plan. Comparison of these percentages and distributions with the flexural behavior indicates that the distribution of the concrete shear area has considerable effect. Panel X, containing only 5 percent horizontal shear area (95 percent insulated), exhibited flexural resistance about equal to that of Panels Y and H with 21 and 15 percent shear area respectively. On the other hand, Panels K and J, also containing 5 percent shear area but concentrated near the panel ends, deflected more than four times as much as the other three and cracked under a much lower load.

The relatively superior flexural performance of these panels containing expanded metal, trussed member, or distributed concrete shear connectors, indicates that such panel designs should be more satisfactory in service conditions than panels without shear connectors. Movements and warping due to loading, or to moisture and temperature differentials, should be considerably reduced over those encountered in panels without continuous shear connection between the shells. However, these advantages may be gained with some loss in insulation value, since either the metal or concrete shear connectors provide a path for heat transfer through the insulation.

Type of shell reinforcement

The flexural behavior as affected by the style of the welded wire shell reinforcement is presented in Fig. 12. The comparison is made between the 2 x 2-14/14 and 6 x 6-8/8 welded wire reinforcement. Panels with each style of reinforcement were made, one each with expanded metal shear connectors and one each without shear connectors. From the data shown, it is evident that with these two types of sandwich construction, the closer 2 x 2 in. spacing held the deflection to a lower level.

The effect of reinforcement style on moment resistance may be partially obscured in these tests. The cracking moments of Panels W and R, with the larger mesh and higher steel ratio, were only somewhat larger than those of Panels G and P, respectively. However, tests performed later than this series indicated that panels containing approximately three times this amount of shell reinforcement may have twice the moment resistance at initial cracking.

DESIGN ANALYSIS

Longer spans require thicker walls in order to provide the moment capacity to resist handling, erection, and wind loads. The moment-deflection relationships of five panels varying in thickness from 2-1/4 to 6 in. and designed with plastic foam insulation and truss-type shear connectors is shown in Fig. 13. In terms of design procedure, the influence of panel thickness on structural behavior is reflected in the moment of inertia, which in turn will control the stiffness or resistance of the panel to deforming forces.

The implications of these sandwich wall tests with respect to panel design are illustrated in Fig. 14 where the test results of 15 panels, 5 in. thick, are compared with two theoretical conditions: (1) the two concrete shells act in a composite manner; and (2) the two concrete shells act independently of each other, or in a non-composite manner. The moment-deflection curves, up to initial flexural cracking, are plotted for these two theoretical behaviors. The structural analyses for these two conditions follow.

Design considerations

The structural analysis of an uncracked 5-in. sandwich wall, 3 x 5 ft, with a 2-in. insulating core and with one layer of 2 x 2-14/14 welded wire fabric in each shell, assuming composite behavior, is as follows:

Moment of inertia—

$$I_c = \frac{1}{12} b (d_o^3 - d_i^3) + 2 (n - 1) A_s d^2$$

where b = panel width, in.; d_o = panel thickness, in.; d_i = insulation thickness, in.; $n = E_s/E_c = (29.0 \times 10^6)/(2.34 \times 10^6) \approx 12$ (See Table 4 for average E_c); A_s = area of shell reinforcement, sq in.; and d = depth of reinforcement to neutral axis of panel, in. Substituting numerical values,

$$I_c = \frac{1}{12} (36)(5^3 - 2^3) + 2 (12-1) (0.090) (1.75)^2 = 357 \text{ in.}^4$$

Cracking moment—

$$M_c = \frac{\sigma_{sp} I_c}{c}$$

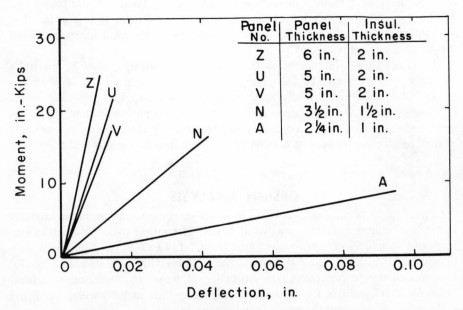

Fig. 13—Flexural behavior to initial cracking as affected by panel thickness for panels with plastic foam insulation and trussed member shear ties

where σ_{sp} = average splitting tensile strength, psi, from Table 4, and $c = d_o/2$. Substituting numerical values,

$$M_c = \frac{296\,(357)}{2.5} = 42{,}300 \text{ in.-lb}$$

Deflection at cracking—

$$\Delta = \frac{5\,w\,l^4}{384\,E_cI_c} = \frac{5\,M_c\,l^2}{48\,E_cI_c}$$

where $w = 8M_c/l^2$; l = span length = 56 in.; and E_c = average modulus of elasticity, psi, from Table 4. Substituting numerical values,

$$\Delta = \frac{5\,(42{,}300)\,(56)^2}{48\,(2.34 \times 10^6)\,(357)} = 0.0165 \text{ in.}$$

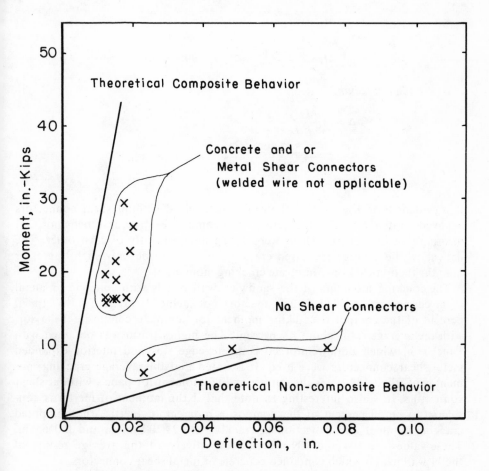

Fig. 14—Theoretical panel behavior compared to test results to initial structural cracking for 5-in. sandwich panels with 2-in. plastic insulation

For non-composite behavior, the analysis of an uncracked 5-in. sandwich wall, 3 x 5 ft, with a 2-in. insulating core, follows:

Moment of inertia—

$$I_{c\ (single\ shell)} = \frac{1}{12}\ bt^3$$

where t = shell thickness. Substituting numerical values,

$$I_c = \frac{1}{12}\ (36)\ (1.5)^3 = 10.125\ in.^4$$

Assuming that both shells deform equally,

$$I_{c\ (panel)} = 2\ (10.125) = 20.25\ in.^4$$

Cracking moment—

$$M_c = \frac{\sigma_{sp}\ I_c}{c}$$

$$M_c = \frac{(296)\ (20.25)}{0.75} = 7,990\ in.\text{-}lb$$

Deflection at cracking—

$$\Delta = \frac{5\ M_c\ l^2}{48\ E_c I_c}$$

$$\Delta = \frac{5\ (7,990)\ (56)^2}{48\ (2.34 \times 10^6)\ (20.25)} = 0.0553\ in.$$

It is evident from Fig. 14 that the wall panels tested without shear connectors behaved similarly to the theoretical non-composite structural behavior, indicating that the concrete shells were acting independently of each other. The data show the average measured cracking moment to be only slightly greater than the theoretical non-composite cracking moment.

The cracking moments of the sandwich wall panels with concrete or metal shear connectors (welded wire connectors not included) range from 40 to 70 percent of the computed cracking moment for complete composite behavior, with the average ratio about 48 percent. The highest ratio was obtained with Panel L in which both reinforced concrete edge ribs and interior expanded metal shear connectors were used. It is noted that this average cracking moment is nearly 2-1/2 times the corresponding moment for panels without shear connectors. It is also interesting to note that if the moment of inertia is considered to be 50 percent of the composite moment of inertia, the computed cracking moment and deflection at cracking are 21,200 in.–lb and 0.0165 in. These values are 104 and 109 percent, respectively, of the average results of the 11 wall panels which contained concrete or metal shear connectors.

In order that the effect of partial composite action might be more readily understood, factors of safety against cracking under a 20 lb per sq ft wind load

TABLE 5—FACTORS OF SAFETY*

Span Length, ft	Factor of safety with respect to flexural cracking	
	Concrete *or* metal shear connectors	Concrete *and* metal shear connectors
8	4.0	5.8
10	2.5	3.6
12	1.7	2.5

*For 8, 10, and 12-ft spans subject to 20 psf wind load. Walls 5 in. thick, with 2-in. insulating cores.

were computed for the more common panel spans of 8, 10, and 12 ft. These factors of safety are shown in Table 5. For each span length, factors of safety for two different panel designs were determined in line with the previous discussion. These designs were: first with the assumption of concrete edge ribs *or* metal shear connectors, and second with these connectors combined. The panel moments of inertia were assumed to be 50 and 70 percent of the composite moment of inertia for each case, respectively.

SUMMARY

In this study of sandwich wall construction, results are reported from thirty-one 3 × 5-ft panels tested in flexure under uniform loading. The more important variables considered were: type of insulation core, type of shear connector (both metal and concrete) between the structural concrete shells, and the panel thickness. In addition, some panels were tested to determine the effect of variation in size and spacing of welded wire fabric reinforcement. The structural efficiency of the various panel designs was assessed by the behavior of each panel at the load causing initial flexural cracking. Considering the almost unlimited combinations of materials which might be used in sandwich construction, and the limitation of this investigation to flexural loading only, it should not be presumed that complete design criteria can be formulated from these tests. However, in spite of the limited nature of the study, several important implications are evident with respect to the chosen test variables.

Adequate shear connection between the concrete shells has been shown to be the predominant factor in obtaining higher values of stiffness and resisting moment in panels with the lighter weight cores. Of the three metal shear connectors used in this study, only the two which had diagonal members significantly improved the structural behavior of the panels.

Properly located concrete ribs provided slightly better structural action in the panels than metal shear connectors. Small concrete posts, distributed uniformly throughout the panel, can produce equal structural behavior with minimum loss of insulated area as compared with the common type of edge and internal solid concrete ribs.

The effect of increased panel thickness is reflected in a larger moment of inertia of the panel. Comparison of the measured resisting moment and deflection at initial flexural cracking with those determined by theoretical analysis has indicated that only partial interaction between the concrete shells may be obtained with sandwich construction. With metal or concrete shear connectors as used in this investigation (folded welded wire type excluded), the measured resisting moment varied from 40 to 70 percent of that computed from assumed composite action. The resistance of panels fabricated without shear connection was only slightly higher than that predicted by theoretical non-composite behavior of the shells. However, if proper shear connectors are employed, design analyses with the assumption of partial composite action have shown that practical panel spans have quite adequate factors of safety against flexural cracking.

From the analyses of the structural behavior at initial flexural cracking, little difference was found between panels of otherwise identical design containing cores of either type of foamed plastic insulation or containing fiber glass insulation. Panels with foamed glass insulation combined with metal shear connectors performed as well as, or better than, those with plastic or fiber glass cores. Panels containing autoclaved cellular concrete cores, even though fabricated without shear connectors, exhibited moment resistance and deflection stiffness generally superior to all other types of panels. This improved behavior is ascribed to the higher modulus of elasticity of the cellular concrete. It is recognized that the insulation values of these different core materials will vary, depending on their unit weight and moisture content.

Closer mesh spacing of the welded wire reinforcement in the shells was effective in reducing deflection under the applied flexural loads.

REFERENCES

1. VanHorn, D. A., and Wilson, K. E., "Structural Behavior of Reinforced Concrete Sandwich Beams," *Engineering Report* 37,. Iowa Engineering Experiment Station, Iowa State University, Iowa City, Mar. 14, 1962.

2. Holmberg, A., and Plem, E., "Testing and Applications of Precast Concrete Sandwich Elements," *Nordisk Betong* (Stockholm), V. 4, 1960, pp. 277–304.

3. Holmberg, A., "Sandwich-Type Structures Made up of Connector-Joined Panels," *Nordisk Betong* (Stockholm), V. 4, 1958, pp. 377–388.

4. Leabu, V. F., "Problems and Performance of Precast Concrete Wall Panels," ACI Journal, *Proceedings* V. 56, No. 4, Oct. 1959, pp. 287–298.

ARCHITECTURAL COMMENTARY

Paper No. 7

This report is a London architect's analysis and commentary on various buildings with precast concrete structural walls and precast concrete curtain walls made on a tour of the United States. British structures are also discussed.

Precast Concrete Wall Panels: Architectural Commentary

By Geoffrey A. Collens

■DURING THE PAST FEW YEARS there has been an increasing interest in the use of prefabrication, system-building, and precasting as aids towards more efficient and faster building. The days are almost past where a simple building will involve special, complex detailing and a multiplicity of materials and trades, creating many problems of dovetailing building operations on the site with the inevitable risk of delays, labor demarcation disputes, and a slow rate of construction.

SYSTEM BUILDING

The use of lightweight prefabricated factory-made structures and components has resulted in faster and cheaper building of schools and similar building types where a relatively short life span is anticipated. In the field of permanent housing, extensive studies and experiments have been made all over Europe to develop precast concrete structural systems for quick and economical house and and apartment construction with special emphasis on multistory work.

Russia, Scandinavia, Belgium, France, and several other countries have all made great progress in the production of factory-made housing units and recently interest in Britain has increased enormously with the emerging realization that the urgent housing needs cannot be met quickly or economically by continuing to rely exclusively on traditional modes of construction. There are scores of new systems appearing on the British market.

The standardization of components and the rationalization of construction has lagged behind in building types where extreme economy is not the paramount aim. This applies to "prestige" buildings as well as standard office buildings, hotels, and university buildings all of which could benefit from some of the lessons of system building for mass production housing. In these instances it seems essential that a reduction in the number of trades involved in putting up a finished building should be one of the main objectives of all architects and engineers.

Towards this aim, coupled with a desire for more expressive architecture than is possible with glass and metal curtain walls, there has been a most promising development of the use of structural precast concrete wall panels. In this and related structural arrangements, the structure and external finished facing can be integrated into a series of standardized units serving a dual function, instead of the finishing materials being applied to an independent steel or concrete frame. Some of the most important and advanced examples of this type of development have been carried out in the United States in recent years. Interest in such developments in growing in Britain at the moment.

SCOPE OF THE REPORT

This report is an analysis and commentary by the writer, a London architect, on various buildings in the United States, where attempts at structural integration have been made. An assessment is made of the advantages, problems, and technical feasibility of a wider use of structural wall panels.

It is not always possible or desirable to draw a hard line between various structural systems and it has been decided to discuss briefly the study of related precast work. This includes nonstructural precast curtain walls, as well as techniques for finishes and manufacture, which are applicable to all precast concrete work whether structural or nonstructural.

This report is largely the result of a tour of the United States, but reference is made to several examples in Britain of structural wall panels. This discussion will follow the author's itinerary.

ARCHITECTURAL COMMENTARY ON STRUCTURES

New York

Fashion Institute of Technology—Cruciform precast wall panels first made a strong impact when used in Banque Lambert, Brussels. That was a prestige building but architects De Young and Moscowitz, with Di Stasio and van Buren as structural engineers, made an economical adaptation of similar principles on the dormitory of the Fashion Institute of Technology (Fig. 1).

The units are 8 ft 9 in. tall by 6 ft wide with joints at midheight of the columns and at midspan of the beams producing cruciform frames (Fig. 2). These structural frames were cast from 5000 psi concrete in steel molds and without special aggregate finish. A simple chamfering of the arms of the cross gives a play of light and shade.

The end of each arm has a steel plate welded onto the ends of the reinforcing bars. In the beam junctions, these plates are welded together but at column junctions this welding is supplemented by dowel and sleeve interlockings which helped with alignment of the frames during erection. The welded junctions produce recessed joints 2 in. wide which were grouted to match the surrounding concrete. To protect the concrete during welding, the architects specified that asbestos or similar shields be used.

The window frames fit directly into grooves at the back of the concrete frame which proved economical and relatively easy to erect. The beams have slots on the inside face to receive the concrete floor slab. Caulking around the windows filled the space between concrete and aluminum frame and allowed for slight movement. The building cost no more than it would have using cast-in-place concrete.

Pan-Am Building—The 59-story Pan-Am Building is the tallest example of a skyscraper completely clad in a precast curtain wall (Fig. 3). The surfaces of all the story-high units were sandblasted to expose the quartz aggregate. Some troubles were experienced over tolerances which were supposed to be 3/8 in. but had to be increased to 1 1/4 in. so the units would fit together without gaps or overtight joints. A curtain wall of this type imposes an extra dead load on the structure, however, lightweight backup was used in panel manufacture to reduce load as much as possible. The building was designed by Emery Roth and Sons, with Walter Gropius and Pietro Belluschi as consultants.

Bankers Trust Building—Close to the Pan-Am Building is the Bankers Trust Building on which Henry Dreyfus worked with Emery Roth and Sons to design a curtain wall of story-high picture frame panels (Fig. 4). These nonstructural units have a sandblasted quartz aggregate finish and are fixed back to the steel structure. The facade pattern is simple and effective. This building achieved a considerable breakaway from smooth metallic curtain walls and is in stark contrast with neighbors.

New Jersey

Rutgers Physics Laboratory—The upper two floors of the physics laboratory of Rutgers University, New Brunswick, N. J., are faced in 84 precast structural wall frames, 25 ft high by 6 ft wide, incorporating four windows in each unit (Fig. 5 and 6). In each frame the central mullion is the main structural member supporting the edge beams and cast-in-place floors. The frames have half-width mullions on each side which are nonstructural and key into the adjoining half mullions of adjacent units. The central mullion has an incised vertical groove so that an effect of split mullions at 3 ft centers is achieved and it is almost im-

Geoffrey A. Collens, associate partner, Derck Lovejoy and Associates, London, studied architecture at Leeds and landscape architecture at the University of Pennsylvania. His tour of the United States in 1963 was made while holding the Arthur Louis Aaron V.C. Memorial Scholarship.

Fig. 1—Fashion Institute of Technology,
New York, N. Y.

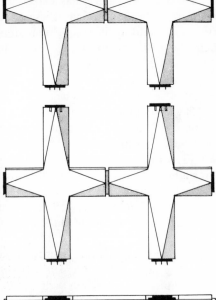

Fig. 2—Precast structural units of Fashion
Institute of Technology, New York, N. Y.

Fig. 3—Pan Am Building,
New York, N. Y.

Fig. 4—Details of panels for the bankers Trust Building, New York, N. Y.

Fig. 5—(below left) Precast structural unit, Rutgers University Physics Laboratory, New Brunswick, N. J.

Fig. 6—(below right) Rutgers University Physics Laboratory, New Brunswick, N. J.

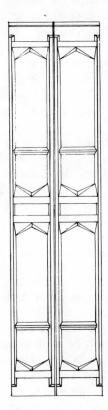

possible to ascertain the width of each precast unit on the facades and consequently any expression of the structural column is completely suppressed.
Although this works well enough structurally and was easy to manufacture and
erect, it is an arrangement which might offend the architectural purist.

Each unit weighs 5 1/2 tons and was made of white portland cement with
Watchung traprock exposed aggregate. The laboratory was designed by
McDowell-Goldstein and Paul Weidlinger was the structural engineer.

Pennsylvania

Philadelphia Police Administration Building—The basic form of the Philadelphia police administration building consists of two circles connected by a
serpentine center wedge which is concave on the entrance side (Fig. 7). The
architects, Geddes, Brecher, Qualls and Cunningham, had previously designed
the Moore School of Engineering for the University of Pennsylvania with a
partial use of precast concrete. From the start they hoped to develop this idea
here and investigated the use of prefabrication to integrate structure, finish,
mechanical, and building services within a single design concept. They decided
that this integration would be possible with the use of repetitive precast elements
designed so that the joints would provide ducting spaces both horizontally and
vertically between the floor and wall members, respectively. Precast concrete
lends itself to complex joints and profiles and has an inherent flexibility with a
possibility of controlled finishes, even when a quick erection program is
required.

The only cast-in-place concrete above foundation level is in the four
elevator-staircase cores to which the precast structure is anchored. The rest of
the superstructure is precast and prestressed. The upper three floors are canti-
levered 12 ft out on precast floor beams which are post-tensioned. The upper
floors are supported on the exterior wall panels and rungs between closely
spaced precast columns on the line of the interior corridors (Fig. 8), so that no
vertical columns obtrude internally. All the floors are of wedge shaped precast
units profiled to provide service ducts and housing for fluorescent lights and
they are left exposed and visible in all the office ceilings. These units are 32 ft
long and have a modified double-T section.

The three-story exterior wall panels are 5 ft wide by 35 ft high, each incorporating and expressing two columns, three spandrels and three window
surrounds (Fig. 9). All these load-bearing wall panels are identical except for
the connecting "ears" which vary according to the service requirements at each
vertical junction. On every fourth panel, the "ear" is wider, thus articulating
the rhythm of the panels and providing space for high velocity air ducts. The
parapet units are separate sections added when the main panels were in place.

All the precast members were manufactured off the site by the shocked concrete process, recently introduced to the United States from Holland. The
vibration process employed produces strong, even textured, dense concrete with
crisp sharp profiles.

Shocked concrete uses a no-slump mixture, with only enough water to
permit chemical reaction with the cement to be completed. The mix is placed in

Fig. 7—Police Administration Building, Philadelphia, Pa.

Fig. 8—Police Administration Building under construction

Fig. 9—Close-up of erection of precast structural panels, Police Administration Building

the forms during the shocking process so that compaction proceeds slowly from the bottom. The aggregate is forced downward and the air and water expelled upwards to eliminate voids even around closely spaced reinforcing bars.

All the exterior surfaces were made from a mixture of white cement, white Maryland sand, and white Georgia quartz. The panels are sealed vertically by butyl rubber compressed between the units as erected and with mastic added afterwards. This allows for expansion and contraction of the building which is an important consideration in a climate which can vary 100 F between the winter minimum and summer maximum.

The precise high quality panels were so well made that few required rejection on arrival at the site and little damage was experienced from site handling, which proved to be quite easy. No drips were detailed in the concrete profiles and to help with weathering, a silicone was applied after the panels had been erected. The glistening white surface has begun to show signs of weathering and streaks are appearing in places not altogether desirable. It remains to be seen whether this silicone treatment has facilitated weathering processes and whether it will make cleaning down at a later date an easy and successful operation. This building is the most completely integrated and significant development so far of structural precast concrete panels.

The structural engineer was David Bloom. August E. Kommendant was consulting engineer.

Insurance Education Center—Two-story wall panels with integral columns, spandrels, and four windows were used on the American Center for Insurance Education, Bryn Mawr, Pa. Each unit, which measures 10 x 25 ft, supports the precast, post-tensioned floor beams which carry a cellular steel floor decking.

At the lower floor, the panels are separated by the air distribution ducts but cast-in-place concrete fillers and dowels extending between the frames provide structural continuity on the upper floor level. All the panels are of intensely vibrated concrete molded in steel forms to give hard smooth surfaces and look well, although the expression of the air ducts between the panels is perhaps over emphatic because of the use of color in this location only.

The architect was Mitchell and Giurgola Associates with Schulcz and Padlasky as structural engineers.

Missouri

Ladue Community Center—Precast frame panels of a basic and economical design were used in the Jewish Community Center at Ladue near St. Louis. Most of them were two stories high with no special finish and although technically and structurally successful, the unfinished concrete is not entirely satisfactory visually. One advantage of precast work over cast-in-place concrete is that it is easier to apply a special surface finish. If no special surface treatment is attempted, the only advantage remaining is speed of erection. The architect was Schwarz and Van Hoefen.

John Hancock Building—Architects Skidmore, Owings, and Merrill, with Paul Weidlinger as structural engineer, used a variation of the cruciform theme of their previous Banque Lambert building in the John Hancock Insurance building in Kansas City (Fig. 10). In this instance the column spacing is much

Fig. 10—John Hancock Insurance Building, Kansas City, Mo.

wider, the cruciform units being 18 ft wide by 12 ft tall which support cast-in-place concrete floor slabs which slot into the backs of the spandrel beams. The whole framework is set forward 4 1/2 ft from the glass wall and makes a magnificent, strong pattern of light and shade over the whole facade.

The concrete has an exposed white quartz aggregate finish of superlative quality with considerable subtlety and great precision in the arrises and junctions. The column junctions have a single dowel fitted into a socket of the column below with the 2 in. recessed joint grouted up and covered by black aluminum. The spandrel joints have no special connections but are simply butt jointed, the 1/4 in. space being caulked to match the concrete. The technical achievement of this building is emphasized by the success in making the large corner sections to the same high standard as the more straightforward units.

The surfaces of the units were ground down to a consistent texture and protected by polyethylene wrapping during the construction processes.

Colorado

Denver Hilton—One of the finest examples of a precast curtain wall is the Hilton Hotel (Fig. 11) in Denver designed by I. M. Pei and Associates. The deeply molded panels for the 20-story hotel were made from a local brown/red granite taken from the building's own foundation excavation and shipped to Salt Lake City to be incorporated into the units.

California

American Cement Corporation Building—An interesting and unusual example of structural precast units is the use of X-shaped members on the American Cement Corporation building, Los Angeles, designed by Daniel, Mann, Johnson and Mendenhall. Eight massive (4 x 5 ft) columns support the tower; load-bearing sunshielding grilles carry two sides (Fig. 12). To reduce superstructure weight in a high seismic zone, all precast and cast-in-place concrete above the fourth floor was of high strength lightweight concrete. A precast screen enclosed the parking section. Glass fiber forms were used.

Fig. 11—Hilton Hotel, Denver, Colo.

The architect is developing this structural grid into a similar design for the Westside Medical Center with precast wall elements 25 ft wide and two stories high. These would support precast floor panels anchored to a central circular core built with slip-form construction. The use of the circle plan standardizes the precast concrete elements, eliminating the special corner members necessary on a rectangular structure.

Engineering Building, University of California—On the Berkeley campus of the University of California, the new engineering building designed by William Wurster was built from a combined system of precast concrete story height panels and cast-in-place concrete columns (Fig. 13). The end flanges of the panels form the permanent forms for three sides of each column and a single board was used for the fourth side. Richly-textured finish was given to the main panel surfaces which makes a change from the rather monotonous use of fine white quartz aggregate on most precast work in the United States.

Washington

Pacific Science Center—No mention has been made so far in this report of the work of Minoru Yamasaki who has exploited the use of precast concrete to heights which were not considered possible a few years ago. His most important design in the writer's opinion is the Pacific Science Center in Seattle (Fig. 14) for whom Naramore, Bain, Brady and Johanson were associate architects and Worthington, Skilling, Helle and Jackson were structural engineers.

All wall panels were prestressed and were either bearing wall panels or curved nonload bearing units. All panels were either 32 or 52 ft high and the

Fig. 12—American Cement Corporation Building, Los Angeles, Calif.

Fig. 13—Engineering, Building, University of California, Berkeley, Calif.

bearing ones had raised tracery patterns incorporated. Most panels were 5 ft wide and all have the same exposed white aggregate. These units support 5 ft wide T-beams for the roof structure with spans up to 113 ft with bolted and welded connections between steel plates cast into the concrete members. It proved no easy task to weld all these joints in such a way as not to damage the precast work and to prevent discoloration, the steel erectors even wore white gloves when handling the panels.

All precast units were steam cured and acid etched to expose the aggregate with a silicone added before polyethylene packaging was added prior to delivery to the site. Some problems arose on the curved units and the joints in the glass fiber molds are just visible as horizontal lines on the taller panels. Another problem was the need to protect all metal connectors during immersion in the acid bath.

The joints have a butyl sponge rod pressed in after erection with a polysulfide base compound sealant on the outside, to provide weatherproof sealing which allows for expansion and contraction in the concrete.

The whole achievement of uniform sparkling white quartz to every member on this building is an example of what factory controlled precast work can attain and it is notable that only one unit was broken during site handling operations.

Civic Center Garage—The Civic Center garage in Seattle (Fig. 15) was the work of engineers Foster and Willard with Kirk, Wallace, McKinley and Associates as architects. Precast spandrel panels and 14-ton prestressed T-girders

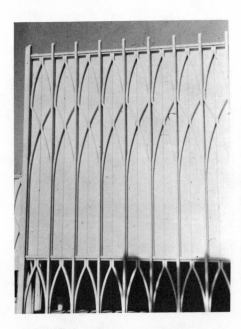

Fig. 14—Pacific Science Center, Seattle, Wash.   Fig. 15—Civic Center Garage, Seattle, Wash.

frame into four-story precast columns spaced on 18 1/2 ft centers. Exposed aggregate surfaces on the panels, cast by the general contractor, provided an interesting effect with the unusual use of brown gravel as aggregate. The aggregate was distributed uniformly over the top of the freshly-cast panels and pushed down flush to the concrete surface by a vibratory screed riding on the edge forms. Sufficient retarder for a 3/8-in. etch was applied. After washing, a beige mortar was broomed into the panels to give a light beige background approximately 1/4 in. deep below the surface of the aggregate.

Minnesota

Medicine Building—Architects Thorsen and Thorshov designed the modern Medicine Publications Building, Edwina, Minn. (Fig. 16), in white precast concrete panels which are much more successful architecturally than those used on their Sons of Norway Building which is faced in story-high panels of black precast concrete. The black panels have not much contrast with the windows which are dark in tone. Similarly shadows are not easily seen and the modeling, therefore, looks flat and the facade monotonous and drab.

The panel units of the Medicine building each consist of two windows, two spandrels, a central mullion, and two half mullions and were cast from 10,000 psi concrete. The forms were in plaster of Paris for the fronts and wood for the sides of the panels.

The units were erected by steel erectors as all connections are welded and problems arose in keeping the panels from becoming stained during welding operations. All joints were sealed by butyl rubber strips being forced in by a screwdriver against a backing, with the exposed face sealed with mastic. Owing to the problem of deliveries of precast units possibly delaying the erection of the building, steel tubular props were introduced so that the floor slabs could be placed before the wall panels arrived on the site. Once the precast units were welded up, the props could have been removed but were in fact left in place.

Fig. 16—Modern Medicine Publications Building, Edwina, Minn.

Wisconsin

IBM Building—The plans of International Business Machines' Milwaukee offices by Harry Weese, architect, and Engineers Collaborative were studied. Apart from the central core, all of this seven-story building is precast, including the floors. The wall panels are 9 ft wide by 11 ft tall with a central mullion, a half spandrel at top and bottom, and half columns at each side, which when joined to the next panels form roughly elliptical shaped columns which are hollow, to take the vertical air supply ducts (Fig. 17). Models of the complex profiled panels were seen at Aggregate Surface's plant at Dearborn, Mich. Difficulties were anticipated in getting the mix around the reinforcement in the thin sections of concrete.

Illinois

Midwest Volkswagen Building—A study was made of drawings for the Import Motors of Chicago office and warehouse building at Deerfield, Ill., with Robert Darvas as the structural engineer and Hausner and Macsai as the architects. The office building has 3 x 5 ft precast units containing a single panel and spandrel arrangement which support the steel roof joists which are connected by welding a channel to a steel plate in the top of each panel (Fig. 18-19).

Michigan

Dearborn Towers—The Dearborn Towers apartments by architects King and Lewis, with Raymond C. Reese Associates as structural engineer, is an 11-story building with the external walls made up of 18 ft 4 in. wide by 8 ft 9 in. tall precast structural wall frames (Fig. 20). Each panel incorporates five windows, four full mullions, and two half mullions (at ends). The frames support the cast-in-place concrete edge beams and the flat plate floor with structural continuity provided by welded connections in the reinforcing. The appearance is simple and a little dull but the system was extremely economical as the panels were fully structural and no applied finishes were needed on this basic framework.

Ford Hospital Garage—To build a flat slab parking garage for the Henry Ford Hospital in Detroit that would fit into a residential neighborhood, Albert Kahn Associated Architects and Engineers made interesting use of "twisted" precast concrete panels (Fig. 21). The panels are hyperbolic paraboloids 24 in. wide at the base and top, 18 in. wide at the waist with a 90 deg twist between top and base. They are nearly 7 1/2 ft high and vary in thickness from 2 1/2 to 3 1/2 in. The panels were cast in glass fiber forms through one edge and vibrated externally on a vibrating table. The concrete used a milky-white quartz aggregate, fine Ottawa sand, and white cement.

Michigan Consolidated Gas Company—The offices of the Michigan Consolidated Gas Company, Detroit, by Minoru Yamasaki and Associates, architects and engineers, is clad in two-story high precast panels (Fig. 22). The members weigh 1 ton each and consist of a mullion and two spandrels to form a "double lollipop." The narrowness of the sections produced a vast number of vertical joints, which are sealed by neoprene double wing seals and caulking. The units were made in Salt Lake City by Otto Buehner and Co. and had to be pre-stressed specially for the 1500-mile journey to Detroit. The edge beams were

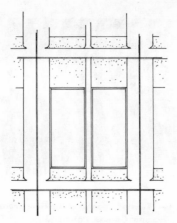

elevation of unit

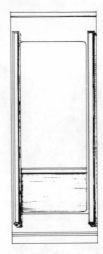

elevation.

typical plan showing panels and half columns

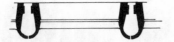

plan of typical precast structural panel.

**Fig. 17—International Business Machines
Building, Milwaukee, Wis.**

Fig. 18—Import Motors Building, Deerfield, Ill.

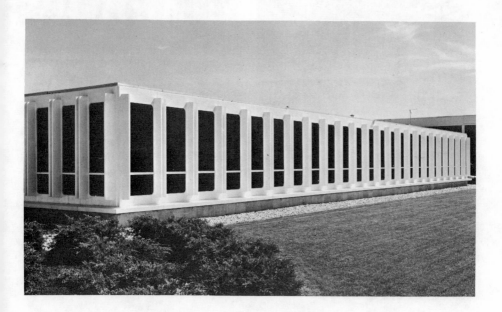

Fig. 19—Import Motors Building, Deerfield, Ill.

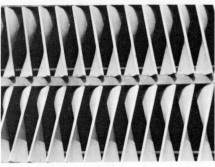

Fig. 20—Dearborn Towers Apartments, Dearborn, Mich.

Fig. 21—"Twisted" panels of the Henry Ford Hospital Garage, Detroit, Mich.

Fig. 22—Michigan Consolidated Gas Company, Detroit, Mich.

Fig. 23—Education Building, Wayne State
University, Detroit, Mich.

strengthened 20 percent to take the extra weight of the precast curtain wall, which will be steam-cleaned annually to keep the glistening, rather wedding-cake-like, appearance intact.

Education Building, Wayne State University—One of the first structural precast buildings by Minoru Yamasaki was the College of Education building, Wayne State University, Detroit (Fig. 23). Load bearing precast concrete "trees" or "lollipops" with exposed white quartz aggregate provide perimeter support to the floor slabs, each one incorporating a structural column and a series of half spandrels. This is a technically successful structural system and the use of 120 units from the same mold makes a fairly complex profile possible and economic, although the styling of the design is not to everyone's taste.

Classrooms and lecture hall, Wayne State University—The newest buildings on the Wayne State University campus are the Meyer and Anna Prentis Building and the Helen L. DeRoy Lecture Hall (Fig. 24), both designed by Minoru Yamasaki and Associates with Worthington, Skilling, Helle and Jackson as engineers.

On the Prentis Building, the same basic "lollipop" system as the College of Education is extended to units 10 ft wide, comprising a central structural column of molded shape with deep half spandrels with faceted profiles and backs rebated to take the cast-in-place floors. With this arrangement, the only joints to be sealed are around the windows which fit neatly into zipped structural glazing gaskets, and at the vertical joints down the center of each spandrel. These spandrel joints have grooves in the concrete to house a tubular neoprene gasket which is adhered to one panel before the next one is butted up. The narrow 3/8 in. joint thus produced is grouted up to match the surrounding concrete.

Fig. 24—Prentis Building and DeRoy Lecture Hall (in foreground), Wayne State University, Detroit, Mich.

Fig. 25—Shapero Hall, Wayne State University, Detroit, Mich. (above)

Fig. 26—Engineering Science Building, Harvard University, Cambridge, Mass. (right)

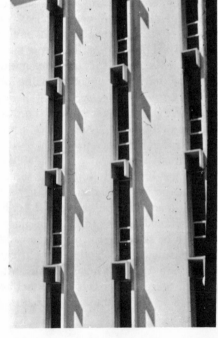

Fig. 27—William James Hall, Harvard University, Cambridge, Mass., under construction

Once again quartz aggregate is used but although not used on the final build-ing an experimental piece of the structure was polished by the precasters to see how that finish would look. The result was a precise molded piece of concrete which rather calls to mind new pentelic marble.

The Helen DeRoy Lecture Hall in the court has incredible, complex, tall wall panels supporting the roof and the profiling is almost Egyptian in character.

Shapero Hall, Wayne State University—Drawings seen for the Shapero Hall of Pharmacy at Wayne State University, Detroit (Fig. 25) by architects Paulsen, Gardner and Associates with Robert Darvas as structural engineer, show this to be mainly a precast structure with 24 ft high precast columns on the bottom two floors with precast wall panels approximately 10 ft square on the upper floors. Steel welded connections are used throughout to provide structural con-tinuity between concrete members.

Massachusetts

Engineering Science Building, Harvard University—The Engineering Science building, Harvard University, Cambridge, Mass., was designed by Minoru Yamasaki and Associates with Worthington, Skilling, Helle and Jackson as engineers. Precast wall units, 50 ft high, with a channel plan shape provide structural support for the floors and clad the entire building in four-story tall panels (Fig. 26). The usual exposed white quartz aggregate is the finish. Glass fiber molds were used and for this length, joints were necessary which un-fortunately are just visible in some places but this problem could be overcome by the use of concrete molds which can be of almost unlimited unbroken and unjointed length. The panels are separated by tall slit windows with precast structural sun shields added at each floor level.

William James Hall, Harvard University—The same architects and engineers as on the Engineering Building have designed the new William James Hall for Behavioral Sciences, seen in Fig. 27 at an early stage of construction. This is a bold structure 16 stories high with huge precast concrete girders 7 1/2 ft deep, with faceted panels on the surface, spanning between widely spaced col-

Fig. 28—Greeley Memorial Laboratory, Yale University, New Haven, Conn.

umns with cruciform plan shapes. Both columns and spandrel girders are finished in white quartz aggregate.

Connecticut

Yale Forestry Building—At the Greeley Memorial Laboratory for the School of Forestry, Yale University, New Haven, Conn., Paul Rudolph, architect, with Henry Pfisterer as engineer, designed four rows of Y-shaped precast columns to support a flat roof composed of 3 ft wide precast units with sculptured coffering visible inside the building (Fig. 28). This is an early example of the use of Y- and T-shaped structural units as a part of the architectural expression and it is a theme now being taken up on building of a more mass production nature such as schools and factories.

Miscellaneous examples

Several other U. S. examples of precast wall panels should be noted. Although not all of them were seen on the tour, they were examined via photographs and drawings.

IBM Building—Gordon, Levin and Associates designed the one-story International Business Machines office building in Kalamazoo, Mich., using structural wall panels, some of which are plain and some contain molded window frames (Fig. 29). The panels were manufactured by the shocked concrete process.

John Hancock Building—The offices of John Hancock Life Insurance in New Orleans (Fig. 30), designed by the same team which designed the firm's Kansas City building, is a somewhat hybrid structure with the concrete elements free from the glass wall to provide sun shielding. The thin but deep columns and transomes are precast and structural but support concrete encased steel beams with a precast facing.

Hillcrest North Medical Center—In the eight-story Hillcrest North Medical Center in San Diego, narrow channel shaped floor-height precast panels provide

Fig. 29—International Business Machines Building, Kalamazoo, Mich.

Fig. 30—John Hancock Insurance Building, New Orleans, La.

Fig. 31—Hilcrest North Medical Center, San Diego, Calif.

Fig. 32—Butler University Library, Indianapolis, Ind.

structural support to the floors together with a considerable degree of sun-shielding (Fig. 31). They are fairly unusual in having cast-in-place connections with the floor slabs in place of the more usual welded steel jointing. The architect was Deems, Martin Associates with A. J. Blaylock and Associates as engineer.

Butler Library—Three-story precast columns support vault units 5 ft wide, 2 ft 9 in. deep, and 50 ft long of precast, prestressed concrete on the Butler University Library, Indianapolis (Fig. 32). Each vault unit weighs 11 tons. Minoru Yamasaki and Associates were the architects and Worthington, Skilling, Helle and Jackson the engineer.

Houston Post Office—Wilson, Morris, Crain and Anderson used precast panels of white cement and quartz aggregate on the Houston Post Office (Fig. 33). Deep mullions provide a degree of sun shading.

BRITISH EXAMPLES

Dock House—St. Katherine Dock House for the Port of London Authority is probably the most sophisticated example of structural wall panels in England so far and obviously derives some inspiration from the Philadelphia Police Administration building. The story-high, one window wide units are either 4 1/2 x 13 1/2 ft or 9 x 16 1/2 ft and have rounded arrises and molded profiles which are easy to withdraw from the casting molds (Fig. 34). Separate parapet units are used at the roof level.

A fairly rough "tweedy" dark gray texture was used on the concrete to provide a suitable surface for weathering in the London atmosphere. Most of

Fig. 33—Houston Post Office, Houston, Tex.

Fig. 34—Panel details for St. Katherine Dock House, Port of London Authority, London, England

the joints are sealed by deflatable neoprene tubing and considerable attention has been given to the detailing of drips and weather checks. The floor slabs and internal columns are of cast-in-place concrete so that the total structural system does not reach the stage of integration found in the Philadelphia Police Administration Building.

The dock house was designed by Andrew Renton and Associates with Ove Arup and Partners as engineers.

New Malden Office Towers—Two 15-story office towers designed by the Architects Department of Planning and Development Ltd. are under construction in New Malden, Surrey. The structural consultants are Samuely and Partners. Use is made of load-bearing, white finished, precast concrete wall units 10 ft high, 15 ft long incorporating three windows on a 5 ft grid, in each unit. Coffered precast floor units span between the precast outer skin and the cast-in-place core structure (Fig. 35).

St. Giles Circus Tower—The office tower under construction at St. Giles Circus, London, will be the tallest precast structure in the world (1965). The architects are R. Seifert and Partners. The polished concrete units are mainly 8 1/2 ft wide and 10 1/2 ft tall, in the form of inverted Y's and provide load-

Fig. 35—New Malden Office Tower, New Malden, Surrey, England

bearing wall panels to the whole perimeter of the building which will rise to 370 ft (Fig. 36).

To attain the cast-in-place concrete characteristics which are favored for buildings of this height, continuity of reinforcement was obtained by using a mechanical joining device in each mullion. The cast-in-place floor slab completes the continuity at each joint. The projection of the units beyond the glass line is 2 ft at the bottom reducing gradually to 1 ft at the top. Erection and jointing is proving fairly simple despite apparent complications upon the drawn details.

Fig. 36—St. Giles Circus Tower, London, England

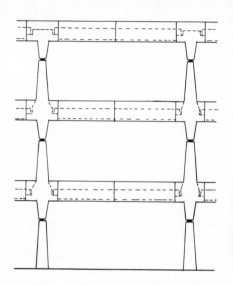

Fig. 37—Elevation of typical three-story bay of H. J. Heinz Headquarters, Hayes Park, Middlesex, England

Fig. 38—Leckhampton House, Corpus Christi College, Cambridge, England

Fig. 39—Leckhampton House, Corpus Christi College, Cambridge, England

Heinz Headquarters—J. Douglas Mathews and Partners in association with Skidmore, Owings and Merrill, with A. J. and J. D. Harris as consulting engineers, designed the H. J. Heinz Headquarters at Hayes Park, Middlesex (Fig. 37). The building looks similar to the Banque Lambert, Brussels, and the John Hancock Building, Kansas City.

Where the John Hancock structure remains a pure system of jointed, tapered column-beam units, the Heinz structure although intended to be similar, was modified during detailed design, although the finished appearance is almost identical to the John Hancock building. The cruciform column units are structural with an integral finish and are connected vertically by a rigid welded steel joint. Horizontally the columns are connected by precast edge beams which are faced by precast cladding panels to match the columns and backed up by cast-in-place concrete floor slabs which provide stability and structural continuity.

Corpus Christi College—Leckhampton House, Corpus Christi College, Cambridge, England, stems from the design by Arup Associates, architects and engineers, for new buildings at Somerville College, prepared 6 years ago. The Corpus Christi structure is a series of white precast H-frames with a light tooled finish to a limestone aggregate. The link is constructed of brick load-bearing walls (Fig. 38 and 39). The walls themselves are of cavity construction, the cavities being used as service ducts.

Somerville was originally designed in 1957 with a cast-in-place frame, where, because of its tooled finish, right angle corners were eliminated. The panels were always designed to be precast. Changing economic conditions and building methods subsequently made it necessary to precast the frame. Corpus, on the other hand, was designed initially to be precast and while embodying many of the principles of the Somerville design, it exploited the structural advantages of an H-frame construction which helped also to eliminate some of the problems of tolerance.

Laingwall System—A system of precast story-height wall units of modular width called the Laingwall system has been developed by John Laing Construction, Ltd. Three examples are shown in Fig. 40-42. The system can be used in buildings up to 16 stories high and a variety of profiles, finishes, and textures are available.

PRECAST PANEL MANUFACTURE

The advance in techniques over the past few years has been so great that it is impossible to report fully on everything which is now possible with precast concrete panels. In the United States, several precasting works were visited to see how various techniques were carried out.

There is now a vast variety of materials being used for molds in precasting: timber, plaster of Paris, rubber, and plastic. Concrete, steel, and glass fiber are finding increasing favor. In the United States, concrete was often preferred because of the large number of castings which can be taken from the same mold and because a panel of almost any size could be cast in a single form without

Fig. 40—Shrewsbury Development Scheme using the Laingwall system

Fig. 41—Shops and offices on Queen Street, Oxford, using the Laingwall system

Fig. 42—Northwestern Gas Board Office, Altrincham, using the Laingwall system

joints. Timber, steel, and glass fiber appear to be the most popular materials for this purpose in England at present.

Aggregates

A hard durable aggregate is desirable, because soft ones will encourage water penetration with the ensuing danger of rusting the steel reinforcing, especially in the English climate. In the United States, the aggregates seen on the tour were mainly white quartz, gray granite, and white gravel, invariably used in fairly fine sizes in a matrix of white cement. In England, there has been a tendency to try far darker panels with rough textures in order to provide suitable weathering surfaces for polluted, damp atmospheres. The use of large knapped flints has been particularly successful in this regard and it is often desirable to look carefully into the matter of sizes of aggregates if a real texture is to be readable from a distance. Small aggregates can give a tone or color, but no apparent texture when seen from a distance.

Texture

There are many possible ways of obtaining textures on precast work. The most dramatic ones are obtained by castings in profiled molds face downwards, or rolling, brushing, tamping, and combing panels cast face upwards.

In the United States, sandblasting and acid etching are the most common ways of exposing aggregate but grinding and bush hammering are also used occasionally.

In England, sprayed or jetted finishes, wire brushing, and washing down with dilute acid are the usual methods employed and the use of sandblasting is nonexistent on precast work to date. Tooled finishes are sometimes applied to precast work but this is one of the more expensive ways to get a good finish.

Coatings

There are several differing points of view on the use of silicones in the United States but the conclusion drawn from discussion was that they should be avoided in most cases. There is no conclusive evidence that their application to precast concrete has any real benefit. On the other hand there is some evidence that silicones help to collect dirt, increase the tendency to streakiness and prevent the more natural weathering of aggregates. The final answers will be known when many years have elapsed so that silicone-treated buildings can be compared with nontreated structures to see how weathering has affected the surfaces.

HANDLING

One of the main arguments put forward against the use of precast concrete is the problem of breakages and the delays to building programs caused by waiting for replacements. In some ways this is an admission of defeat, for all building materials should be handled with proper care and if this is done, breakages will be few. One answer is to precast units on the site, which is now done quite often in England. It has the disadvantage that for extra high quality products, factory controlled casting is necessary, using all the best machinery and methods, which cannot always be installed in a precasting plant on the site.

The design of large precast units should be done with the type of crane or lifting apparatus in mind so that the system is economically feasible and uses the site equipment close to its capacity. For transport to the site it is sometimes necessary to provide extra reinforcing or prestressing just for the journey. Thought must also be given to the provision of lifting hooks, eyes, and bolts to ensure that precast units can be manipulated easily on site.

Once on the site, problems often arise over the erection of precast concrete and as welded connections are frequently employed, steel erectors normally do this work in the United States. This site work usually falls within the mason's responsibilities in England and obviously demarcation disputes can soon cancel out the advantages of precasting unless they are settled at an early stage in every contract.

CONNECTIONS AND JOINTS

In the United States, connections are usually welded steel junctions whereas in England more use is made of bolted connections and cast-in-place concrete junctions to provide structural continuity. With welding there is need for adequate tolerance, for careful detailing to provide space for easy welding and for strict attention in the field to avoid scorch marks on finished surfaces.

Joints

The best type of precast wall unit is that which reduces the number of joints to be weatherproofed to a minimum. The three-story wall units of the Philadelphia Police Administration Building show how dozens of joints normally associated with windows, sills, columns, beams and spandrels can be eliminated if all these elements are cast in a single precast panel. The use of cruciform column/beam structural elements reduces jointing to midspan and midheight positions which are fairly easy to detail.

Although handling and breakages may influence one against large precast units, the simplification of weatherproofing by the reduction of joints is a strong counterargument to be taken into consideration.

The use of mastics has given rise to many problems in weatherproofing especially because of their lack of permanence. In England the problem is especially serious owing to penetrating rain needing to be kept out. Complex weather checks, water bars, and flashings have been developed in order to try and solve this difficulty.

In the United States there has been a rapid development of synthetic joint sealing materials for curtain walling and these are now used extensively for jointing of precast panels both structural and non-load-bearing. These materials come in numerous forms: tubes strips, winged sections and more complex shapes (Fig. 43-44). Sometimes they are made to adhere to one concrete panel before the next one is put in place and the joint tightened up. In other cases they may be forced into place after the panels are in position. The different methods used have been referred to in the relevant descriptions in the main

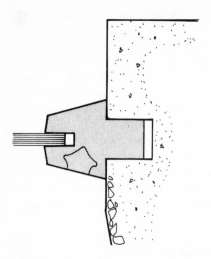

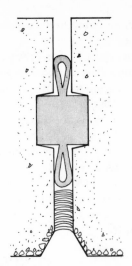

Fig. 43—Typical glazing detail with structural
neoprene zip gasket acting as window frame
in precast unit

Fig. 44—Half-size detail of winged neoprene
joint gasket

text of this report. So far very little use has been made of these materials in
England.

PANEL SIZE

Opinions differ widely concerning the economic height for precast structures. The consensus of opinion of engineers with whom this was discussed,
was that 15 to 20 stories was about the maximum reasonable height. This is
partly due to the difficulty in providing structural continuity in precast work.

In most designs all wall panels would be the same size to make the most of
repetitive molds, but this means that on a multistory building the panels at the
lower floors are the only ones fully working while the topmost ones are much
underused, structurally and oversized physically.

In the case of the tower at St. Giles Circus in London this height limit has
been doubled to 370 ft which is more than any engineer spoken to on this tour
said was likely at present. To overcome the wasteful oversizing of panels there
is a steady diminution up the height of the building. This is done in thickness
only so that the basic mold remains unchanged in profile with the thickness as
the only varying factor.

A particularly suitable height for precast structural wall panels is three to
four stories as it is possible in these cases to have precast units the full height
of the building, with total elimination of horizontal joints.

CONCLUSIONS

From this report it can be seen that only a small beginning has been made
towards the use of precast concrete for the dual purpose of structure and

finished cladding. The future possibilities of development on these lines are enormous but use of this material in this way must be seen in proper perspective.

There are many cases where this use of precast concrete is correct and desirable but there are others where various factors make it uneconomic or impractical. One of the most difficult problems to be overcome is the possibility of a whole building site coming to a halt because the precast structural members have not arrived on time. With the increasing use of system building and factory made prefabricated building parts it is obvious that this criticism, often leveled against precast work in particular, will soon be applicable to all building operations using factory fabricated products as the main structure.

This problem like most of those in the building industry can be solved with proper organization of building methods and programing.

ACKNOWLEDGMENTS

The tour and resulting report was made possible by the Arthur Louis Aaron V.C. Memorial Scholarship. The assistance of the many architects, engineers, precasters, and technical organizations contacted before and during the tour are gratefully acknowledged. The author's own photographs were supplemented by the Portland Cement Association; Robert C. Cleveland, Fig. 31; Hank Snock, Fig. 34; Colin Westwood, Fig. 38 and 39; and John Laing and Son Limited, Fig. 40, 41, and 42.

APPENDIX I—TESTS

Tests for Precast Wall Panels

Reported by Subcommittee V, ACI Committee 533

J. A. HANSON
Chairman

RICHARD C. ADAMS
RICHARD A. BACHUS
VICTOR F. LEABU

W. H. F. SAIA
HARRY T. SWANSON
C. D. WAILES, JR.

This report is submitted for discussion prior to preparing a recommended practice. Emphasis is placed on those specification and production control tests and procedures which have led to confusion among architects, engineers, prefabricators, and owners. Tests for compressive strength and for freeze-thaw durability are discussed. Standard 6 x 12-in. cylinders are recommended for compressive strength samples wherever such procedure is practical. Otherwise, 4-in. cubes are suggested, the test results of which should be reduced 20 percent as an estimate of cylinder strength. Due to the vertical orientation of most wall panels, specification of freeze-thaw testing is not recommended generally. The report recommends that wall panel concretes should be air entrained without specification of a fixed percentage of air content. A preliminary list of needed research is included.

FOREWORD

In order that ACI Committee 533 may most efficiently accomplish its mission, the committee has been divided into six subcommittees as follows:

Subcommittee I — Design
Subcommittee II — Methods
Subcommittee III — Materials
Subcommittee IV — Types
Subcommittee V — Tests
Subcommittee VI — Miscellaneous

It is expected that each of these groups will develop their appropriate part of a final report or recommended practice by the committee as a whole. Considering the diversity of wall panels as presently produced, it is evident that much effort and time will be required by its subcommittees before achieving this goal. Therefore, to more rapidly disseminate the information, individual subcommittee reports may be issued at an earlier time. It is probable that the material considered in some of the subcommittees might duplicate and overlap that of others. As an example, it may be difficult to clearly separate the work of Subcommittees III and V, particularly in the area of specifications for materials. In recognition of these circumstances, this report has not been prepared as a complete presentation of all tests that may be required for satisfactory wall panel production. The subject material presented has been considered to have the most immediate importance to the industry. After discussion of these primary topics, definite test recommendations are presented with the expectation of beneficial discussion prior to final inclusion in a recommended practice.

INTRODUCTION

Architects, designers and producers of precast concrete wall panels have become well aware of the variety of, and at times contradictory, tests that have been specified for the fabrication, installation, and serviceability of these units. Perhaps the greatest discrepancies and confusion arise from the size of test specimens. Many precasting plants utilize cubes for compressive strength control tests by reason of convenience and economy. On the other hand, most architects and engineers are familiar with 6 x 12 in. cylinder tests. Clarification of test result interpretation should accomplish considerable elimination of controversial issues that sometimes develop between architect-engineers, testing laboratories, and the precast panel manufacturer.

Testing for precast concrete wall panels might take on many facets and be quite extensive. On the other hand, it is known that many prefabricated panel buildings of all sizes are now under construction and many more than that are on the drawing boards. Considering the variety of panel types used in these structures, a complicated series of tests would only add to the uncertainty and confusion that already exists. Consequently, this subcommittee has agreed that its recommendations should lead to basic, simple test procedures that can be interpreted precisely and easily. Only by these means can the high quality and durability of precast wall panels be assured. In accordance with this philosophy, the tests to be recommended for wall panels have been separated into two categories: tests for specification and control purposes and those for research.

It is emphasized that, in the formulation of the recommendations of this report, only panels fabricated with concretes containing aggregates comparable to usual structural quality have been considered. It is not intended that these recommendations would necessarily apply to panels with exposed surfaces of concretes containing aggregates generally employed in insulating concretes, or of cellular concrete, although it is recognized that these excepted panel materials may become more widely used in the future.

ACI Committee 533, Precast Concrete Wall Panels, was organized in 1961 to develop recommendations or specifications for the design, manufacture, handling and erection of precast concrete wall panels. This progress report of Subcommittee V has resulted from deliberations of the subcommittee at three meetings in 1962 and from full committee consideration at the ACI fall meeting, Seattle, and at the annual convention, Atlanta.

SPECIFICATION AND CONTROL TESTS

ASTM specifications

The following ASTM test methods and specifications and those cited in this report are intended to cover the main requirements for each item involved, including all current revisions to such tests or specifications.

C-31 — Concrete Compression and Flexure Test Specimens, Making and Curing in the Field

C-192 — Concrete Compression and Flexure Test Specimens, Making and Curing in the Laboratory

C-42 — Hardened Concrete, Securing, Preparing, and Testing Specimens from, for Compressive and Flexural Strengths

C-260 — Specifications for Air-Entraining Admixtures for Concrete

C-175 — Specifications for Air-Entraining Portland Cement

C-185 — Test for Air Content of Hydraulic Cement Mortar

The subcommittee has separated the considerations of specification and control tests into two subcategories of interest: compressive strength and durability of the concrete.

Compressive strength

Types of test specimens—The task of this subcommittee was greatly simplified by the recent revisions of ASTM C 31 and C 192, Methods of Making Concrete Specimens in the Field and the Laboratory. These revisions extend the recognized requirements for the consolidation of 6 x 12 in. concrete specimens to include internal or external vibration. Such action now allows the preparation of standard test specimens from concrete mixtures in the low slump and zero-slump range. Many mixtures used in precast panel plants fall into these types and these producers can now provide compressive strength data on a basis that will be readily accepted by engineers, architects and owners of structures. The subcommittee definitely advises the use of the 6 x 12 in. cylinder test in all cases that are practicable. Since wall panel concretes are generally in the high strength category, it is particularly important that the cylinder ends be capped with materials of higher strength, or be lapped plane, in accordance with the corresponding requirements of ASTM C 31 and C 192. Test values of compressive strength should be evaluated on the basis of "Recommended Practice for Evaluation of Compression Test Results of Field Concrete (ACI 214)."

In the past, the compressive strength of wall panel concrete has been often measured with cubes varying in size from 1 to perhaps 6 in.

Measured values of compressive strength generally increase rapidly as the sample size decreases, provided a relatively representative and homogeneous sample is obtained. On the other hand, if the small specimen should happen to contain a large piece of aggregate, the measured strength may decrease rapidly. These and other similar conditions have led to much confusion and unacceptance of cube test results.

There are cases in wall panel construction where the strength of cylindrical test samples may not sufficiently represent the strength of the panel concrete. An example of this insufficiency may exist where a relatively thin facing layer is cast with a mix containing a high volume of coarse aggregate for architectural appearance. These mixes often require high water contents for proper consolidation. In this case the facing layer is often backed with an extremely dry concrete which effectively removes the excess water, leaving a highly durable and pleasing finish to the exposed face. In such cases, cube tests may furnish a more satisfactory set of data than would the cylinder test. The subcommittee recommends the use of 4-in. cubes, fabricated in a manner to reflect the improvement of the facing mix water-cement ratio (see later section for one method of such sample preparation). This cube size was chosen to accommodate aggregate sizes up to 1½ in. and to minimize the undesirable aspects of small test samples on compressive strength. If the wall panel concrete contains aggregate larger than 1½ in., the test samples should be prepared as cylinders of appropriate diameter and length.

The 4-in. cubes may be prepared as individual specimens or may be sawed from 4 in. thick slabs if this procedure is more convenient. The quality of molds, consolidation methods, finishing, and curing of the cubes or slabs should adhere closely to the similar requirements for 6 x 12-in. cylinders, (ASTM C 31 and C 192). Most of the requirements of these standard methods can be applied directly to cube preparation and testing. Some slight deviations will be required in the consolidation of the concrete as a result of the different specimen size. Considering the 4-in. depth, it would appear reasonable to place the concrete in a single layer. Tamping or external vibration methods would then proceed as outlined in the designations. Similar to the restrictions for cylinders of 4-in. diameter or less, internal vibration should not be applied to the consolidation of individual cubes. This method would be applicable, however, to casting of 4 in. thick slabs. ASTM C 42 for sawing of beams from hardened concrete should be used as a guide.

Ratio of cylinder strength to cube strength—It is well known that compressive strength measured using cubes is generally higher than that measured with 6 x 12-in. cylinders. In line with the desire to eliminate, as far as possible, confusion and misunderstanding between the various elements of the wall panel industry, the subcommittee has investigated the propriety of a standard ratio of the strengths measured by these two types of test samples. It is recognized that this ratio has long been the subject of much controversy between engineers, research people and others. Nevertheless, from a practical viewpoint, the future development of wall panels requires such a factor. Furthermore, the factor should be chosen sufficiently conservative to satisfy specification agencies, and yet not be unduly restrictive to those panel prefabrication plants that usually establish compressive strengths on the basis of cubes.

The magnitude of this ratio may be affected to some extent by many variables, such as relative sizes of specimens, quality of concrete, type and amount of aggregate and perhaps others. It appears that the overriding cause of the varying test results from the two types of samples, given uniformity of mix and consolidation, may lay in the shape factor (including the ratio of longitudinal and lateral dimensions) and in the relative amounts of restraint offered by the testing machine platens. With these considerations in mind and in view of considerable test data available for a wide range of concretes, the subcommittee determined that a standard factor might be established by means of which compressive strength results from cubes could be interpreted as 6 x 12 in. cylinder strengths.

Lyse and Johansen[1] have perhaps presented the most complete single study of the relative results of strengths obtained from cubes and cylinders. They tested about 850 specimens of concretes ranging in compressive strength from 2100 to 6400 psi. The specimen sizes (in centimeters) nearly corresponded to 4, 6, and 8-in. cubes and 4 x 8 and 6 x 12-in. cylinders. The cylinders were cast both vertically and horizontally. The comparison specimens were tested at 28 days after continuous moist curing. They concluded (within this test series) that quality of concrete had no effect on the ratio of cylinder strength to cube strengths; the average strength of vertically cast cylinders was 86 percent of the strength of the cubes; and the average strength of horizontally cast cylinders was 80 percent of the cube strength.

Swanson* has furnished tests of 72 concrete specimens with a nominal 6 x 12 in. cylinder strength of 6400 psi. Cubes, 3 in., and 3 x 6, 4 x 8, and 6 x 12-in. cylinders were tested at 7 and 28 days after continuous moist curing. Table 1 shows the ratios of compressive strengths of each size of cylinder to that of the 3-in. cubes.

Pfeifer† compared the ratio of 3 x 6 and 6 x 12 in. cylinder strengths to that of 4 in. cubes. His study included 26 specimens cast from an architectural concrete mix containing white portland cement, white Ottawa sand, and ⅜ to ¾ in. crushed marble aggregate. Two values of com-

---

*Correspondence between ACI Committee 533 and H. T. Swanson, Universal Atlas Cement Division, United States Steel Corporation, Aug. 1962.

†Correspondence between ACI Committee 533 and D. W. Pfeifer, Portland Cement Association Research and Development Laboratories, July 1962.

TABLE I—CYLINDER-CUBE COM-
PRESSIVE STRENGTH RATIOS
(SWANSON)

Age of testing, days	Cylinder size		
	3 x 6 in.	4 x 8 in.	6 x 12 in.
7	0.93	0.91	0.84
28	0.91	0.88	0.81

TABLE 2—CYLINDER-CUBE COM-
PRESSIVE STRENGTH RATIOS
(PFEIFER)

Concrete quality, psi	Cylinder size	
	3 x 6 in.	6 x 12 in.
5000	—	0.88
7200	0.94	0.88

pressive strength, 5000 and 7200 psi were included. The cube specimens were sawed from 4 in. thick slabs. Both cylinders and slabs were consolidated by vibration. Testing was performed at 28 days. Pfeifer's values of the cylinder-cube ratio are shown in Table 2.

Consideration of these data has led the subcommittee to recommend that 80 percent of the measured cube strength be used as an estimate of the strength of the same concrete when tested as a 6 x 12-in. cylinder.

Special types of cubes—The compressive strength of products produced in some precasting plants may not be well represented by cubes or cylinders as discussed previously. Many of these plants have developed special types of cubes to more properly measure the compressive strength of their concrete. This situation has been recognized by the subcommittee and the use of these special cubes is encouraged, provided that the strength correlation to the standard cylinder test can be demonstrated. As an example Pfeifer also studied the cube strength of his 5000-psi concrete when used with a dry, expanded shale, "back-up" concrete. In this case, a layer of the architectural concrete, with a 6-in. slump, was vibrated in the bottom half of an 8 in. deep slab form. This was covered immediately with 4 in. of the dry structural lightweight concrete. After curing sufficiently, the facing concrete was cut from the back-up concrete and sawed into 4-in. cubes. The compressive strength results at 28 days were 5610 psi for the facing concrete cast without the back-up layer and 6430 psi for the same concrete cast with the backing. The data indicates that the strength of the facing concrete was improved 15 percent by withdrawal of excess mix water into the dry lightweight concrete.

Curing of test samples—The type of curing and test ages for compressive strength test samples has been discussed thoroughly by Subcommittee V. It is recognized that continuous moist curing may provide the best measure of the potential strength development of a particular concrete mix. On the other hand, a few days of moist curing followed by storage at approximately 50 percent relative humidity may more nearly correspond to average curing conditions of wall panels. However, these "average" conditions are seldom achieved for more than a short time at any particular geographical location. Ambient weather conditions vary widely over the continent. ASTM C 31 and C 192 chosen as standard for wall panel samples, specify moist curing and recommend certain test ages for laboratory cast specimens depending on the type of cement. Further, it is the desire of the subcommittee to simplify the interpretation of test results as far as possible. Therefore, the subcommittee recommends that curing and age of testing of compressive strength samples, for either specification or product control purposes, be in accordance with the above appropriate recommendations of ASTM.

In this connection, it is suggested that individual precasting plants may advantageously set up routine tests for compressive strengths, regardless of job specifications. A day-to-day record of even a single sample per day may serve as a desirable quality control procedure, providing strict control of sampling, curing and testing is rigidly followed. Such data, accumulated over a period of time, might serve to indicate to architects, engineers, and owners the high quality and uniformity of the output of that particular plant.

Acceptance tests of finished products—As architects, engineers and precasting plants develop and understand the use of the above recommended procedures for simplified test specimens, rejection of finished wall panels should decline to a minimum. However, even under the best regulated procedures, questions may arise as to the adequacy of a certain panel or series of panels. Under these conditions, it is the judgment of the subcommittee that the actual concrete in the suspected panel is the best indication of the quality of the panel. The quality of the actual concrete can be most dependably established with the use of core tests.

ASTM C 42 provides standard procedures that may be adapted to coring the panel and for conditioning and testing of the samples. For most convincing test results, the length-diameter ratio of the core sample should be obtained as near to two-to-one as possible. ASTM allows these ratios to be as small as one-to-one and provides for adjustment of measured strength for any ratio between these values. The core holes can often be adequately patched without damage to the appearance or structural integrity of the panel.

The rebound hammer test has not been accepted by ASTM as a standard test for hardened concrete and therefore should not be used as an acceptance test for precast concrete wall panels. The rebound hammer has been found to be useful, however, in making qualitative comparisons of hardened concrete in place. The committee suggests that at least six readings be averaged to obtain a value for any given location in a panel and that readings be taken on a 2-ft grid when an over-all survey of any given panel is desired. Such a survey may serve as a useful guide for location of representative core samples if these are considered necessary.

Durability

Freeze-thaw testing—Vertical wall panels are in a most favorable orientation to achieve a high degree of durability. The vulnerability of concrete to freeze-thaw damage depends on the degree of saturation and since wall panels are subjected to only occasional wetting, it is seldom that a high degree of saturation would be achieved. The coincidence of freezing conditions and a high degree of saturation may occur even more rarely. Another favorable durability factor inherent with wall panels, is the general prevalence of high compressive strength which is a requirement for the practical and economic operation of wall panel plants. Such high strength allows early stripping and reuse of forms and more satisfactory attainment of architectural finishes. The influence of high compressive strength on durability is accomplished through the associated property of low permeability. For assurance that this desirable strength protection may always be obtained, this subcommittee would recommend to Subcommittee I, Design, that the minimum compressive strength of exterior surface concrete be at least 5000 psi when tested as 6 x 12-in. cylinders at 28 days.

A number of older structures, located in regions which experience many cycles of freezing and thawing annually, provide reassuring direct evidence of the durable quality of precast panels. The Baháí Temple of Wilmette, Ill., may be one of the more well-known examples. The superstructure of this most ornate building was erected about 25 years ago. Precast concrete panels of exposed crushed quartz were backed up with cast-in-place concrete. Several thousands of visitors each year attest to the beauty and high quality of this structure. In nearby Skokie, Ill., the Portland Cement Association has an outdoor panel display dating from 1937 and 1938. This variety of exposed aggregate surfaces was obtained by the use of the aggregate-transfer method. In spite of the severe weather conditions in this area and the rigors of a move from its original location to the new PCA Laboratories, the high strength concrete in these panels is completely free from cracking, no aggregate pieces have fallen, and the architectural appearance of the panels is as desirable now as when fabricated. It may be interesting to note that these examples predate the use of air entrainment in concrete.

More recently, laboratory confirmation of the durability of high strength, impermeable concretes has been obtained. Isberner[2] studied the frost resistance of several facing concretes and demonstrated their durability, even under severe conditions of exposure. His panels were fabricated from concretes having strengths varying from 10,000 to 13,000 psi at 28 days. The concrete mixes contained three types of quartz, two brands of white portland cement, and the aggregates in the panels were exposed with a surface retarder. Both air-entrained and non-air-entrained concretes were included. The samples were first subjected to the realistic exposure conditions of freezing and thawing in air with water flushing of the exposed surface prior to each freeze. After 125 cycles none of these panels exhibited deterioration. Further discussion of the durability of these laboratory panels, when subjected to overly severe freezing conditions, will be continued under the subject of air entrainment.

Consideration of these and other examples of the native frost resistance of precast wall panels has led to the conclusion that freeze-thaw tests are not generally required for specification purposes. Such tests are expensive, time consuming, and the applicability of such test data to actual conditions is often prone to misinterpretation. At times, some panels such as those located at ground level, may be subjected to freezing conditions along with a high degree of saturation or to splashing by deicing salts. These conditions may lead to deterioration. Ground level panels that are thermally insulated by snow would not fall in this category. If, in the opinion of the specifying agency, freeze-thaw tests are required for panels in these special environments, the subcommittee recommends the system of freezing and thawing in air with water flushing prior to each freezing operation. This method is considered to be both realistic and applicable.

Air entrainment—The test series by Isberner[2] included both air-entrained and non-air-entrained concretes. After successful exposure to the test conditions considered most realistic, the quartz aggregate panels were frozen and thawed with the exposed face immersed in water at all times. This is, of course, a most severe and abnormal test condition and one which would not be encountered with vertical panels. This rigorous procedure was followed to reveal the differences in durability of the air-entrained and non-air-entrained concretes. After 350 cycles, additional to the original 125, the air-entrained concrete panels were in perfect condition, while the non-air-entrained concretes were severely deteriorated.

A fixed level of air content in the low slump, high cement content, often harsh, mixtures used in wall panels, is difficult to achieve without excessive use of air entraining agent. Amounts of air-entraining agents much greater than normal dosage may lead to frothiness of the paste, segregation and finishing problems, and also to retardation of strength development. In the Isberner tests, the air-entraining agent was added to the mix only in the amount that would be used in normal cement content mixes with good workability. The air contents, measured by linear traverse, in the air-entrained and non-air-entrained concretes were 3.52 and 3.46 percent, respectively, an insignificant difference. However, the tests of the hardened concrete also showed that while the non-air-entrained concrete had 10,000 voids per cu in., the void count of the air-entrained mix was raised to 137,000. Thus, the air-entraining agent functioned to break up the large accidentally entrapped air bubbles into much smaller air voids which provide freeze-thaw protection.

In recognition of these difficulties and possible detrimental effects, the specification of a fixed air content is not recommended for wall panel mixes. On the other hand, in view of the additional benefits of higher durability and workability, the subcommittee strongly recommends the use of a "normal" amount of air-entraining agent or of an air-entraining portland cement in all concrete mixtures used for wall panels. A "normal" amount of air-entraining agent, as considered in this report, is that dosage which will provide 19 ± 3 percent air in a 1:4 standard sand mortar (ASTM C 175, Table II).

The specification of the amount of air-entraining component to be used (in contradistinction to specification of a fixed percentage of air entrainment in the wall panel concrete) may be accomplished by reference to three ASTM designations. Where the panel manufacturer chooses to use an air-entraining white or grey portland cement, ASTM C 175 can be directly adopted. Where a non-air-entraining portland cement is to be used, the addition of a recognized air-entraining agent in the proper amount is advisable. ASTM Specification C 260 and Test Method C 185 will be helpful guides in this regard.

.There is sufficient technical evidence to indicate that the application of some waterproofing or water repellent materials to the surface of a durable concrete does not increase the resistance to frost action. Maximum durability to freezing and thawing deterioration is achieved by the use of integral air entrainment as mentioned above. If the waterproofing or water repellent materials are applied for other purposes, their behavior should be fully evaluated prior to construction to assure satisfactory performance. This evaluation would require actual job materials and exposure conditions.

Absorption—Absorption tests for concrete have often been specified in the past in the view of obtaining and demonstrating a higher degree of durability. Actually, a number of investigations have failed to reveal more than an uncertain and devious relationship between absorption of concrete per se, and the frost resistance of that concrete. In an important study of the influence of aggregates on durability, Verbeck and Landgren[3] have gone far towards explaining the relationship between aggregate characteristics and durability. This paper is suggested study material for anyone concerned with the manufacture of prefabricated panels or with the design and specification of any concrete mixtures. They have convincingly demonstrated that durability of the concrete, given a paste of sufficient air entrainment, depends, not on the level of total absorption of the aggregate and paste, but on the rate at which the aggregate becomes "critically saturated." Critical saturation occurs in a paste or aggregate when 91.7 percent of the void space is filled with water. This saturation is "critical" in the sense that the remaining voids may not be able to accommodate the 9 percent expansion of water during freezing. The rate of critical saturation will depend on the ability of the aggregate void structure to resist saturation and to relieve hydraulic pressure as water freezes in the voids. A saturated aggregate of low porosity may accommodate the expansion of freezing pore water by simple elastic action. An aggregate of high porosity will tend to relieve these disruptive pressures, particularly if embedded in an air-entrained paste. However, if the aggregate is frozen so rapidly that sufficient time is not available for this beneficial pressure reduction to occur, deterioration may result, provided that the rock is critically saturated. This situation appears to seriously question the applicability of the severe, rapid-type laboratory tests for the frost resistance of concrete. It also indicates the inapplicability of simple concrete absorption tests as a measure of durability.

Standard tests of absorption such as those presented by ASTM C 67, may have merit, however, in other situations. These tests might be adapted to serve as a relative measure of the ability of different concretes to resist dirt adherence, staining from soft aggregates, fading of colors, or other phenomena that may lead to nonuniformity and unsightliness. More research information needs to be gathered on the adequacy of absorption tests to fulfill this function.

RESEARCH

The subcommittee has considered a number of research projects, listed below, which should lead to valuable information relevant to satisfactory and economical concrete wall panels. It is realized that many of these are now under study at the Portland Cement Association Laboratories, at various prefabrication plants, by many government agencies, and by universities and colleges. The early publication of results of these studies and the undertaking of others is strongly encouraged. The subcommittee welcomes suggested additions to this list.

RECOMMENDED RESEARCH PROJECTS

1. Studies of sandwich panel construction
   - (a) Amount and type of shear ties
   - (b) Effects of various types of insulation
   - (c) Amount and types of shell reinforcement
   - (d) Cracking of thin shells due to restraint of thickened sections
   - (e) Warping due to differential moisture and temperature
   - (f) Thermal characteristics (also for solid panels)

2. Tests for load bearing panels
3. Long-time durability of panels
   (a) Whole panels of various finishes
   (b) Effects of the wide variety of fabrication methods
   (c) Effects of the wide variety of aggregates used

4. Absorption as related to staining and other types of nonuniformity, including the effects of protective coatings

5. Fire testing of solid and sandwich constructions

6. Cause and prevention of efflorescence

7. Capacity and design of inserts

8. Methods of joinery

9. Proper joint fabrication

10. Thermal and moisture effects in complete wall assemblies

11. Caulking materials

RECOMMENDATIONS FOR SPECIFICATION AND CONTROL TESTS FOR PRECAST CONCRETE WALL PANELS

Compressive strength

1. Standard 6 x 12-in. cylinders of concrete should be used for compressive strength tests at all times that preparation of such specimens is practical. Preparation and testing of the test cylinders should be in accordance with the requirements of ASTM C 31 or C 192.

2. If 6 x 12-in. cylinder preparation proves impractical, compressive strength specimens may be fabricated as 4-in. cubes. These cubes may be molded individually or cut from slabs. Preparation and testing of the specimens should be as nearly consistent with the above requirements of ASTM as possible, with the exception that the concrete be placed and consolidated in a single layer.

3. The maximum size of aggregate in concrete tested as 4-in. cubes should not exceed 1½ in. If larger size aggregate is contained in the concrete, compressive strength should be measured using standard 6 x 12-in. cylinders.

4. If cubes are used as compressive strength test specimens, the average strength of the cubes at any test age should be multiplied by the factor 0.8 to arrive at an estimate of the corresponding cylinder strength. Both of these values should be reported.

5. The subcommittee recognizes that certain wall panel producers utilize special cubes that may be more representative of their particular products. It is recommended that this practice be followed, provided that the strength correlation to standard 6 x 12-in. cylinders can be demonstrated.

6. Curing of compressive strength specimens should be in accordance with ASTM C 31 or C 192 (moist-type curing), except in those cases

where the corresponding wall panels are given accelerated curing. In these cases, the test specimens should be cured, as nearly as possible, similar to the product.

7. Acceptance tests for compressive strength of doubtful panels should be confined to tests of cores. Test cores for compressive strength should be prepared, conditioned, tested and reported in accordance with the requirements of ASTM C 42.

8. Subcommittee V recommends to Subcommittee I, Design of Precast Concrete Wall Panels, that the finish concrete of exterior panel surfaces should have a minimum compressive strength of 5000 psi at 28 days when measured with 6 x 12-in. cylinders in accordance with ASTM C 31 or C 192.

9. Subcommittee V suggests that individual producers of panels might institute day-to-day determinations of compressive strength of their product with samples in accordance with Recommendations 1 through 6. The records of this routine sampling would well serve quality control and demonstration purposes.

Durability

10. It is the opinion of the subcommittee that, due to the vertical orientation, freeze-thaw durability tests of wall panels are not required for specification purposes. If, in particular circumstances, such tests are deemed desirable, it is recommended that the tests should consist of freezing and thawing in air with water flushing of the surface prior to each freezing cycle.

11. A specified level of air content in many architectural concrete mixtures is difficult to obtain while preserving high quality in the paste. Consequently, in view of the vertical location of wall panels, the specification of fixed levels of air content in the panel concrete is not recommended.

12. The use of air-entraining cements or air-entraining agents in the concrete for precast wall panels is recommended. The amount of air-entraining agent in the cement or in the concrete mixture should satisfy the requirements of ASTM C 260 or C 175 when tested in accordance with ASTM C 185. These requirements will result in 19 ± 3 percent air in a 1:4 standard sand mortar.

REFERENCES

1. Lyse, Inge, and Johansen, R., "An Investigation on the Relationship Between the Cube and Cylinder Strengths of Concrete," *RILEM Bulletin* No. 14, Mar. 1962, pp. 125-133.

2. Isberner, A. W., "Durability Studies of Exposed Aggregate Panels," *Journal,* PCA Research and Development Laboratories, May, 1963, V. 5, No. 2, pp. 14-22. Also *Research Department Bulletin* 158, Portland Cement Association.

3. Verbeck, G., and Landgren, R., "Influence of Physical Characteristics of Aggregates on Frost Resistance of Concrete," *Proceedings,* ASTM, V. 60, 1960, pp. 1063-1079.

This report was submitted to letter ballot of the entire committee which consists of 14 members; 9 members returned their ballot of whom 9 voted affirmatively and none negatively.

Received by the Institute Aug. 12, 1963. Title No. 61-24 is a part of copyrighted Journal of the American Concrete Institute, Proceedings V. 61, No. 4, Apr. 1964. Separate prints are available at 60 cents each, cash with order.

American Concrete Institute, P. O. Box 4754, Redford Station, Detroit, Mich. 48219

APPENDIX II—SI UNITS

APPENDIX II

TABLE OF CONVERSION FACTORS: BRITISH UNITS TO SI UNITS*

Multiply	By	To Obtain
Length		
Inches	25.4 (exactly)	Millimeters
Feet	30.48 (exactly)	Centimeters
Yards	0.9144 (exactly)	Meters
Miles (statute)	1.609344 (exactly)	Kilometers
Area		
Square inches	6.4516 (exactly)	Square centimeters
Square feet	0.092903 (exactly)	Square meters
Square yards	0.836127	Square meters
Volume†		
Cubic feet	0.0283168	Cubic meters
Cubic yards	0.764555	Cubic meters
Capacity†		
Liquid pints (U.S.)	0.473179	Cubic decimeters
Gallons (U.S.)	3.78543	Cubic decimeters
Cubic feet	28.3160	Liters
Mass		
Ounces (avdp)	28.3495	Grams
Pounds (avdp)	0.45359237 (exactly)	Kilograms
Short tons (2000 lb)	907.185	Kilograms
	0.907185	Metric tons
Force/Area		
Pounds per square inch	0.070307	Kilograms per square centimeter
	0.689476	Newtons per square centimeter
Pounds per square foot	4.88243	Kilograms per square meter
	47.8803	Newtons per square meter

*Selected conversion factors from "ASTM Metric Practice Guide," American Society for Testing and Materials, January, 1964. Available from ACI headquarters.

The metric technical unit of force is the kilogram-force, which is defined as the force which, when applied to a body having a mass of 1 kg, gives it an acceleration of 9.80665 m/sec/sec. The metric unit of force in SI (Systeme International) units is the newton, which is defined as that force which, when applied to a body having a mass of 1 kg, gives it an acceleration of 1 m/sec/sec. These units of force must be distinguished from the inconstant local weight of a body having a mass of 1 kg. However, because it is general practice to use "pound" rather than the technically correct term "pound-force," the term "kilogram" has been used here instead of "kilogram-force" in expressing the conversion factors for force.

†Laboratory volumetric apparatus in the United States is calibrated in milliliters rather than cubic centimeters (1 ml = 1.000028 cu cm).

Multiply	By	To Obtain
Density		
Pounds per cubic foot	16.0185	Kilograms per cubic meter
	0.0160185	Grams per cubic centimeter
Bending Moment or Torque		
Inch-pounds	0.011521	Meter-kilograms
	1.12985×10^{6}	Centimeter-dynes
Foot-pounds	0.138255	Meter-kilograms
	1.35582×10^{7}	Centimeter-dynes
Foot-pounds per inch	5.4431	Centimeter-kilograms per centimeter
Velocity		
Feet per second	30.48 (exactly)	Centimeters per second
Miles per hour	1.609344 (exactly) ...	Kilometers per hour
	0.44704 (exactly)	Meters per second
Flow		
Cubic feet per minute	0.4719	Liters per second
Gallons (U.S.) per minute	0.06309	Liters per second
Work		
British thermal units (Btu)	1055.06	Joules
Btu per pound	2.326 (exactly)	Joules per gram
Power		
Horsepower	745.700	Watts
Btu per hour	0.293071	Watts
Foot-pounds per second	1.35582	Watts
Heat Transfer		
Btu in./hr ft^{2} deg F (k, thermal conductivity	1.442	Milliwatts/cm deg C
	0.1240	Kg cal/hr m deg C
Btu/hr ft^{2} deg F (C, thermal conductance	0.568	Milliwatts/cm^{2} deg C
	4.882	Kg cal/hr m^{2} deg C
Deg F hr ft^{2}/Btu (R, thermal resistance)	1.761	Deg C cm^{2}/milliwatt
Btu/lb deg F (c, heat capacity)	4.1868	J/g deg C
Ft^{2}/hr (thermal diffusivity)	0.2581	Cm^{2}/sec
Fahrenheit degrees	5/9 (exactly)	Celsius or Kelvin degrees

INDEX

INDEX